Repair of
Wooden Boats

**John
Lewis**

Repair of
Wooden Boats

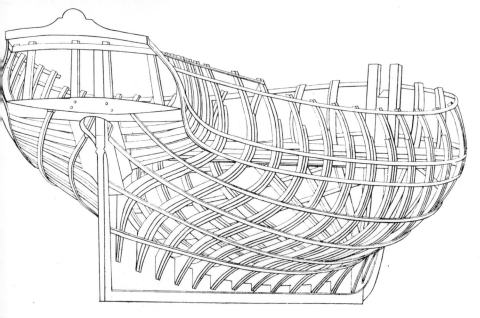

David & **Charles**
Newton Abbot . London . North Pomfret (VT) . Vancouver

ISBN 0 7153 7378 1

Set in 10 on 11 Bembo by Ronset Limited
and printed in Great Britain
by Redwood Burn, Trowbridge and Esher
for David & Charles (Publishers) Limited
Brunel House, Newton Abbot, Devon

Published in the United States of America
by David & Charles Inc
North Pomfret, Vermont 05053, USA

Published in Canada
by Douglas David & Charles Limited
1875 Welch Street North Vancouver BC

Contents

Charles Harker at work fitting new deck
planks on *Iris*, his Colchester oyster
dredger. Note also new stempost,
breasthook, bitts and deck beam.
Clamps are essential for such work
(*Keith Mirams*)

Introduction

Fitting out and working on one's boat is not only the best way to get to know what condition she is in, but also the way to increase one's affection for her. Old wooden boats inevitably need repairs and replacements. This may mean dealing with heavy timbers in old fishing boats or precise and intricate joinery in finely built yachts.

Boat-repair work is no more difficult than cabinet-making or many forms of household joinery. It does, however, have certain fundamental differences, mainly because all fastenings have to withstand strains from every direction and not, as with house carpentry, just gravitational pull; and the materials used, whether timber or fastenings, have to withstand damp, rot, corrosion, electrolysis and wood-boring crustacea.

This presupposes that repairers of wooden boats have some joinery skill, and more than some if they are planning to do major repairs to yachts built by first-class boatyards. On the other hand, to replace a frame in an old fishing smack is mainly a matter of commonsense, plus a certain amount of physical strength, or at least dexterity. The latter is probably more important than the former. I learned much about dexterity from a shipwright who was virtually one-handed. He was Bob Brewster, who worked in Frank Knights's yard in Woodbridge in Suffolk.

Bob Brewster was not only a fine example of how to come to terms with adversity but he also was the source of much of the information in this book. A dozen years or so before he died he had a crippling stroke that left him paralysed down his right side. His right arm remained almost useless, but, even so, with the help of his fellow shipwrights he taught himself to do practically all his work with the other arm. Within five years of his stroke he was building fishing boats with only minimal assistance. He used to say that no matter how handicapped you are, if you have the right tools and know how to use them, almost anything is possible.

This last sentence goes to the heart of the problem. You must have the right tools, and in boatbuilding there are certain special tools. You must not only know how to use them but also how to care for them. Backed with that knowledge, this book should be a pointer to how various boat-repair jobs can be tackled and what timber and fastenings are needed for such work.

The Repair of Wooden Boats is the result of over 30 years of boat-ownership, which has included both the repair and conversion of boats. The information given in the following pages, apart from my own modest findings, has been gathered from shipwrights and boat-restorers, professional and amateur, with whom I have worked or talked on both sides of the Atlantic.

Repairing one's own boat is a sure way of getting to know her better. No matter how old or how battered she may be, the work of putting her into good shape is its own most satisfying reward.

PART
ONE
*Assessing
the Problem*

I

Surveying

If it is an old boat freshly painted, view it with suspicion. If the bottom of a boat is cemented inside, and it is not a fishing smack, also view it with suspicion. Fishing boats were often cemented as soon as they were built and there is rarely any trouble under the cement. Any rot will be along the planks or frames where they abut on the top of the cement.

If the inside of a boat is lined throughout, remove the lining to see what lies behind it. One is likely to find rot in such places as the timber-heads; at the end of the deck beams and the covering board, particularly if it is pierced to take bulwark stanchions; the knightheads etc. One or two rotten beams can be dealt with quite easily, but it is a major operation to replace a rotten deck shelf.

If the boat smells badly, it is probably suffering from wet or dry rot. Dry rot has a pungent smell.

Rot and Decay So-called wet rot fungi, such as *Coniophora cerebella*, produce dark stains on the surface of the wood and yellow streaks under the surface. Different species of *Poria*, such as *Polyporus sulphureus*, *Poria vaillantii* and *Poria xantha*, are all forms of wet rot found in old boats. *Polyporus sulphureus* is often found in the heart wood of oak trees.

If infected timber is used in boatbuilding, conditions usually favour the growth of the fungus. The only possible treatment is to cut out the infected timber. White or cream coloured growths on the surface of the timber, together with fine white strands, indicate the presence of these *Poria* species.

Merulius lacrymans, the so-called dry rot, grows in places that are damp *and* badly ventilated. It can be recognised by a grey bloom over the surface of the wood, which soon begins to look charred, with a surface broken up into a regular pattern of transverse and longitudinal shakes. The spores can reach every part of the boat, and the rot's greyish strands can spread over paint and metal in search of bare wood. Without moisture the fungus cannot live; nor can it live below water, for it needs oxygen.

To deal with wet or dry rot remove all affected wood, and paint the nearby timbers with two coats of an organic-solvent-based preservative, such as Rentokil Dry Rot Fluid. Then fumigate the boat by mixing 9oz of potassium permanganate with 1 pint of formalin in a bucket and leaving the mixture in the boat for several days, with all the entrances blocked up. After that, open up and air for several days.

Rot nearly always comes from fresh water, either from condensation or from rainwater leaks. Where it is difficult to remove affected timbers that are still structurally sound, drill them in a staggered fashion and force in a fungicide under pressure.

Staining under varnish, which is usually caused by fungi, can be prevented by brushing on two coats of an organic solvent preservative before varnishing.

In an old boat the first thing you have to look for is rot. *Top*, decay by wet rot fungus, *Polyporus sulphureus*; *Lower*, decay by dry rot fungus, *Merulius lacrymans* (*The Forest Products Research Laboratories*)

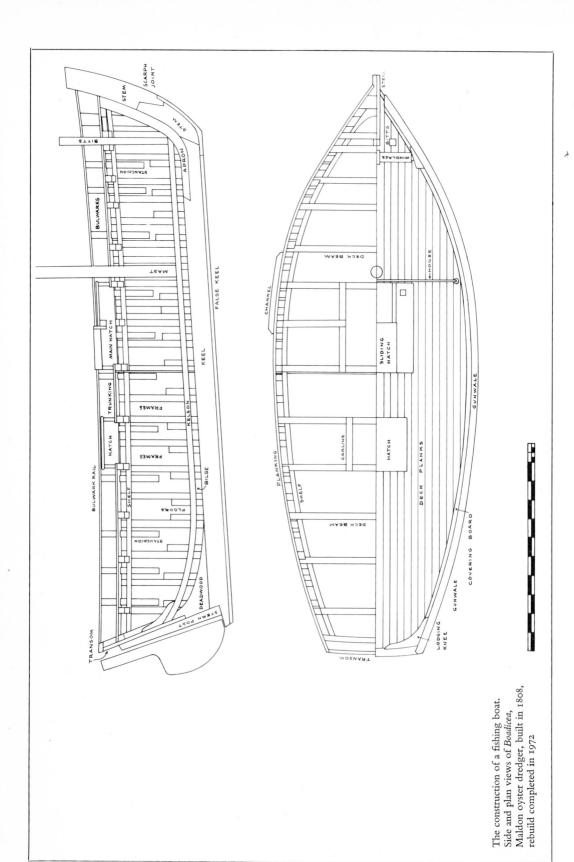

The construction of a fishing boat.
Side and plan views of *Boadicea*,
Maldon oyster dredger, built in 1808,
rebuild completed in 1972

Wood-borers Gribble (*Limnoria lignorum*) is a crustacean (resembling a woodlouse) about $\frac{1}{8}$in long, which makes burrows about $\frac{1}{10}$in wide in the planks and timbers of boats. It does not penetrate much below the surface, but can cause considerable damage to planking and to rudder trunks. An even worse borer is the mollusc *Teredo navalis*, which is found in some European waters. The teredo, like the gribble, bores along the grain and can be detected, as can the gribble, by hammering and pricking. The bottom of a boat that is badly infested with these borers will have to be replanked.

Tar varnish is a better deterrent to wood-borers than anti-fouling. Wood-borers flourish in salt water; a boat moved to fresh water will lose its borers, as will one left on shore for some months.

In the restoration of any old boat all new timber should be treated with preservatives such as Rentokil Dry Rot Fluid or Brunophen, which have maximum penetration; or the timbers should be pre-treated with a water-based copper-chrome-arsenate (CCA) preservative, applied by vacuum pressure. This can be done only at special treatment plants, and the timbers should be machined, cut and drilled before receiving treatment.

Parts of an old vessel and materials used in remedial treatment

Apron: The backing timber inside the stempost. The planking is not normally fastened to the apron, so it is fairly easy to take out this timber if it is rotten. In small boats like dories the planks are fastened to the apron and cut off flush, so that a stempost can be fitted to cover the plank ends. With old fishing boats and some other old craft, if the hoodends have gone, the planks can be fastened to the apron, trimmed flush, and a stempost fitted dory-fashion.

Bilge: The space below the floorboards. Rot may be present in the floors and at the foot of the frames. If the boat is concreted, examine timbers and planking along the top edge of the concrete. There is often trouble here, but rarely below the concrete if the boat was concreted when built.

Bitts: A frame made up of two heavy pieces of timber that pierce the foredeck and are through-bolted to a deck beam just forward of it, and are seated on the boat's floors or apron. The square mortices in the deck are packed with wedges. The forward pull of the anchor cable, which is belayed to the bitts, is taken by substantial knees bolted to both the bitts and the deck. A horizontal beam is fitted to the after side of the bitts. The most likely place for rot is where the bitts pierce the deck and where they meet the floors.

Breasthook: This horizontal timber helps to bind the forward end of the ship together. It is through-bolted to the stem and locked to the forward frames. It is subject to rot from leaks in the deck. It is not possible to take it out without removing the deck planks or breaking it up. It can be replaced with a forged-iron or strap-steel breasthook.

Bulwarks: The sides of the ship above the deck and the most common point of fungal decay in old ships. This decay occurs where the stanchions penetrate the covering board, and may be transmitted to adjacent timbers or bulwark planking. If only one or two stanchions have rotted, it may be sufficient to cut away the decayed timber, scarph in a new piece of covering board and fit a dummy stanchion on top. Very small areas of decay can be cut away and filled with marine glue or pitch.

Details of structure of deck, beams, frames and topsides in fishing boat

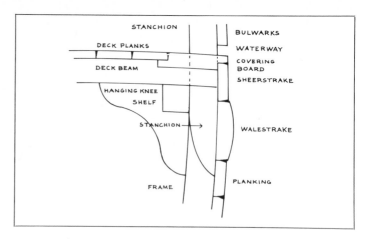

Butt strap:
: A rectangular piece of planking used to back up a butt joint in topside or deck planking; also used for backing up graving pieces that may have been let into the deck planking.

Cabin trunkings:
: The sides of the deck-houses often show signs of water softening along their lower edges. Any evidence of leaks inside should be a warning of this. If the softening has not gone too far, allow to dry out thoroughly, removing any quadrants that may be fitted between the bottom of the trunking and the deck. Scrape out or cut away any soft wood, soak in fungicide and then bed down new and reasonably sized quadrants in plenty of mastic. The screws must not be screwed diagonally into the joint but horizontally into the cabin sides or vertically into the deck.

Carlines or carlings:
: Structural timbers to which the sides of the deckhouses and hatches are fitted. Areas of rot may be found where leaks have occurred; if they are not extensive, the affected timber can be cut away and made good. If the carlines are in a bad way, the cabin trunk will have to be lifted and the carlines replaced. Pitch pine is a better timber than oak for this purpose, as it is less subject to rot.

Caulking:
: The method of filling the seams in deck or topsides with oakum or cotton. When seams are leaking, rake out the old caulking, clean the seams, taking care not to open them unnecessarily, re-caulk then paint them with a seambrush and thick lead paint.

Ceilings:
: The lining of the ship. When surveying old boats, you will find it necessary to remove a certain amount of this. Ceilings should never be carried right up to the deckhead. Leave two or three inches at the top and drill largish holes below bunk level for ventilation.

Centreboard case:
: In old vessels that have sailed hard leaks may be evident along the foot of the case. It may be necessary to lift the case and rebed and refasten it.

Chainplates:
: Metal straps fastened either to the outside or (with modern yachts) to the inside of the vessel's topside. If these are made of steel, they are almost certain to have rusted, and their fastenings to have corroded. In a major refit it is best to remove them, and, if they are not too worn, to have them regalvanised before refastening.

Coachroofs:
: The roofs over deckhouses, if canvas-covered, often have areas of rot below the canvas. If you have reason for suspicion, or if the canvas is bubbling, lift, clear up any areas of rot, dress with fungicide and re-cover with new canvas.

14

Corner posts:	These are fitted at the corners of deckhouses. The sides may be lap-jointed when the post comes inside or rabbeted into the two sides. This is the better construction, for it avoids exposing the end grain of one of the planks, as happens in a lap-joint. If the corner post has rotted, it probably means rebuilding the deckhouse, or at least one end of it.
Counter:	A rounded or square-ended stern that projects aft of the rudder, and one of the most likely spots in an old boat to harbour decay. In old yachts, with long counters harbouring rot, there is often a case for reducing the length of the counter by sawing off the last 2–3ft. This will get rid of part of the rot, and make the rest of the infected timber that much easier to get at.
Covering board:	The outside deck plank covering the timberheads. This is usually the first part of the deck to go, because of rainwater getting through where the stanchions may pierce it. If rot is only present in small areas, these can be cut away, treated with fungicide and fitted with graving pieces.
Decks:	With a laid deck, check for leaks below and particularly along the covering boards, hatchways and trunking. In a very old boat, when, through movement, the deck opens up, the most economical solution is to cover the deck with marine ply and the marine ply with GRP (see below). The marine ply will stiffen the boat, and the GRP will make it watertight. Alternatively, lay thin planking over the marine ply. If the decks are very worn, remove all the deck planks and any deck beams that have decayed, replace the latter and replank with teak or fir.
Fastenings:	If the ship is iron-fastened, look for rot in the timber round the fastenings, particularly in mahogany. Examine for rusty or loose nails. If copper-fastened, see that the rooves are hard up against the timbers. If they are not, it may merely mean that the timber has shrunk, and in that case if is quite a simple matter to harden up the rooves. If the vessel is nail-sick, that is, if the fastenings have corroded badly, it may mean refastening the entire vessel.
Floors:	The frames that support and tie the keel. If the floors have decayed badly, it is not too difficult a task to take them out. If they have to be broken up to get them out of the vessel, make careful templates. If floors have to be replaced, the kelson, if the boat has one, will have to be shifted. It will be bolted through the floors to the keel.
Frames:	The timbers or ribs to which the planks are fastened. These timbers are either steamed or sawn. Steamed timbers frequently break at the turn of the bilge. Usually it is easier to double them up, with a new timber alongside the broken one, rather than to take out the broken timbers. With sawn frames, if these have decayed badly, it is better to take them out. In taking out old frames it would be wise, as in the case of floors, to make a template of their shapes before removing them. They can then be chiselled out in small bits. New frames can be cut from grown crooks; from two or three short straight lengths of timber, or cut from $\frac{3}{4}$in marine ply and side-laminated, which is certainly not traditional but is an effective method of construction.

The frames of most fishing smacks are not checked into the keel, but merely up to it. These frames are sometimes joined by short floors scarphed into them or heavy floors held up against them and sometimes side-bolted to them. |
| *Garboards:* | The planks that are rabbeted into the keel. When replacing floors or kelson, you will find working easier if you remove garboards, as clamps can then be pushed through from under the vessel. (If the |

planking and kelson are in good order, one would not consider such an operation!)

Glues, resin: Synthetic glues have replaced natural glues in boat work. They have to be used with a hardening agent. Beetle A, Aerolite 300 and Cascophene RS 216M are different types and brands of resin glues.

GRP: Glass-reinforced plastic (so-called fibreglass).

Gudgeons: Metal eyes on the after end of the sternpost to sternport the rudder pintle. These need examining for corrosion, particularly for electrolytic action.

Section through gunwale and topsides in a clinker-built ship's lifeboat

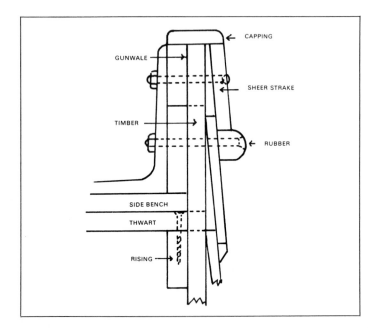

Gunwale: The timber that extends round the top edge of the topsides of a small craft. This is one of the first places to rot in an open boat. Repairs and replacements are relatively simple.

Hatches: These frequently need replacing in old vessels. They often show movement at the joints and softening of the trunking where it abuts the deck. Hinges of lifting hatches have a limited life. When fixing new hinges, make certain that they have bronze and not steel pins.

Hoodends: The fastenings (usually screws) at the fore or aft ends of the topside and bottom planking.

Hull: If any major replacements have to be made to the hull of an old craft, it is important to prevent that hull from going out of shape. If the keel has to be removed, complete any reframing first and, to conserve the shape, fit temporary bilge keels to take the weight of the hull while the old keel is being taken out. If concrete ballast has to be removed, chip it out with a cold chisel. In a rebuild it does not matter what damage you do, but if it is a matter of only replacing a few floors, it is worth taking care not to damage the structure of the boat.

Keels and keel bolts: The replacement of a keel in an old boat is about the biggest operation, apart from a complete rebuild, that anyone could undertake. In fishing boats the most one would usually have to do would be to replace a false keel that might be frayed, or even have pieces missing. In any old

16

boat one or two keel bolts should be withdrawn, to verify their condition. The fact that they look all right at the head is misleading, for they may have wasted away in the middle. If the boat has a steam or an internal-combustion engine, there is rarely any rot below it, presumably because of the preservative effects of dripping sump oil.

Kelson: The longitudinal timber lying on top of the floors, to which the keel is bolted. You should find no difficulty in shifting the kelson if it needs replacing, or if you have to get at the floors.

Knees: Supports made from natural grown crooks, or from laminated wood' side-laminated marine ply, or forged steel strap. Lodging knees are for vertical support. Knees contribute greatly to the strength of a vessel, and it may be worthwhile putting in additional knees to stiffen an old vessel.

Kingplank: The centre plank in a foredeck with a laid deck. The kingplank is virtually a structural member and may be heavier than the rest of the planking.

Pintles: The metal pins on a rudder, which fit into the gudgeon to form a hinge on which the rudder can swing. Look out for looseness or wasting away either from wear or electrolytic action.

Planking and sheerstrakes: If these have to be replaced, it is advisable to use freshly felled timber. The planks can then be drawn into position with tackles and cramps. To fasten them to the frames, drill and countersink and drive home flat-point iron nails, or copper nails, and clench. Look along the waterline to see if there is any rot, and examine the garboards for the same reason.

Rooves or rubs: Small round copper washers used in fastening copper nails. In old vessels these may need hardening up – by means of a hollow punch and a ball-pein hammer.

Rubbing strake: Protective planking or timber to withstand chafe round the topsides of a vessel. The section of a rounded rubbing strake is important. The top surface should slope downwards, to prevent fresh water lodging along the top.

Rudder trunk: The trunk or tube through the counter of a vessel that carries the rudder post. If properly engineered, it will present no problems, but if the trunk is made of wood, there is almost certain to be rot in it. Often there is no means of getting at the caulking inside it. The best thing to do is to take it out, replace it with a bronze tube and fit a bronze shaft to the rudder.

Samson post: A single bitt, stepped on the apron, to which the anchor cable may be belayed. As samson posts are subject to some considerable strain, it is important that they are securely supported, by means of knees, etc.

Shaft log: A stout hardwood chock fitted to the inside of the planking to take the stern tube and inner gland bearing. In old boats these frequently show signs of deterioration, either from rot or from heavy shakes.

Shelves or sheerclamps: Longitudinal timbers to which the ends of the deck beams are fastened. If the shelf has decayed, a major rebuild will be necessary. It is probably the most difficult timber to move in a vessel.

Spars: The masts, yards, booms, gaffs and bowsprit of a vessel. When examining these, you may ignore longitudinal shakes, provided the wood has not rotted inside the cracks. These shakes should be cleaned out, dried and plugged with soft filling. In addition to a spike for pricking soft or rotten wood, a hammer is useful, for a soft tap on good wood gives a sharp note, but a tap on rotten wood a more muffled sound. Old gaff-rigged vessels often have broken gaff jaws. Renewal is a simple task. Spruce masts will need copper sheathing as a protection against chafe from the gaff jaws.

Details of the stem of a ship's lifeboat, showing apron and kelson. The breasthooks are of steel strap

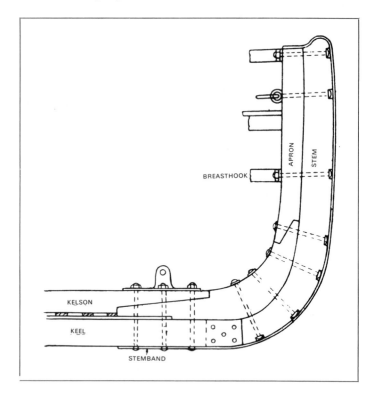

Stem: Examine hoodends to see that the screws are firm. If the screws are made of brass, they may well have dezincified and will have to be replaced. If the hoodends are frayed, the stem damaged or the apron has rot in it, fit a new apron and fasten the ends of the planks to this. Remove the old stem, cut off the plank ends flush with the front of the apron and fit a new stempost overlapping the apron by the thickness of the planking, thus providing a rabbet for the hoodends.

Stockholm tar: A wood tar (as opposed to coal tar) useful as a preservative for timber as well as for treating natural fibre ropes.

Stopwaters: Long cedar plugs of about $\frac{1}{2}$in diameter used in scarphed and butt joints. After cutting and rounding, the stopwater is smoothed off by being driven through a die made from seasoned oak. The drill that is to be used for drilling the holes through the joints is used to drill the die. After smoothing, the stopwater is driven home.

Tar varnish: This can range from tar bought from the gasworks to a slightly refined bitumastic paint. Useful for steel craft because of its anti-corrosive properties. A mixture of tar varnish (80 per cent) and creosote (20 per cent) makes a tolerable anti-fouling.

Templates: Pattern made up from cedar planks or hardboard.

Tie rods: Rods of bronze or galvanised steel connecting cockpit or cabin trunk carline to the shelf (sheerclamp). Each end of the rod is threaded and held in position with a nut and washer. Tie rods are also used in a fore and aft position to prevent deck beams from spreading, particularly in the way of the mast.

Transom: A type of stern made up of one or more planks athwart the sternpost, to which the ends of the topside planks are fastened.

Trowel cement: A filler made up in proprietary forms and used to smooth out abrasions or unevennesses in a surface that is to be painted.

Waterway: A channel for the escape of water and a possible spot for surface softening.

2

Setting Up for Major Repairs

Setting up the hull for major repairs. The level of the waterline is obtained by means of a water-filled length of ⅛in-diameter plastic tube (C), with a ½in-diameter glass tube (A and B) at either end, which is fixed at the fore and after ends of the waterline. The hull is shored up by means of chocks (D and E) screwed under the channels or to the wale strakes, and with two supports (F and G) screwed to the stempost and to a transverse baulk of timber (H) on the ground. The athwartships level is achieved by hanging a plumb line from the stemhead

When one has to do major repairs or alterations, one's first task is to shore up the boat so that her waterline is level. This can be done by measurement from the ground (if the ground is more or less flat) or it can be done with an aqualevel. This is quite a simple gadget, consisting of a length of plastic tube not more than ⅛in in bore, with about 18in of glass tube at either end. The plastic tube should be about 3ft longer than the boat. The whole is filled with water so that when the glass tubes are held upright and together, the water may come halfway up the glass. Now, with the glass tubes held at each end of the boat, near the waterline, it is easy to see whether the boat is level or not.

Once the boat is level fore and aft, the next thing is to ensure that the stempost and sternpost are upright. For this purpose, use a plumb bob. When the boat is upright, brace the stem and stern from the side of the shed.

If the work has to be carried out in the open, lay a piece of timber on the ground at right-angles to the boat immediately under the stemhead, This timber needs to be something like a railway sleeper, about 8ft long. about 12in wide and 4in thick. Make sure that the stemhead is vertical

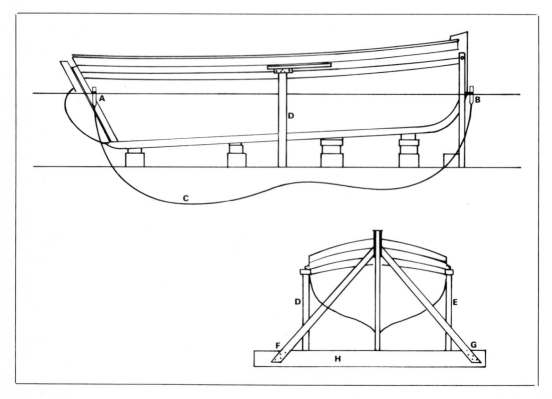

Whaler conversion chocked up for repairs (*J. D. Rogers*).

Building up a fin keel for a whaler conversion (*J. D. Rogers*)

by means of a plumb line, and brace it to the timber on the ground with two supports. Tackle the stern in the same way.

If the work is being done on your own ground, it is worthwhile building some kind of temporary shed over the boat. The simplest form of protection could be a framework of steel scaffolding (which can be hired) roofed with corrugated iron sheets and protected at the sides by sheets of polyethylene. Secure these sheets firmly against the wind.

Alternatively, if the work is done in a mud berth or on a hard, you could build up a wooden framework from the deck and cover it with heavy-duty clear polyethylene. Canvas tarpaulins would of course provide adequate cover, but would have to be folded back when you were working on deck. Polyethylene on the other hand admits plenty of light.

If the work has to be done in hot or drying weather, it is advisable to drape tarpaulins over the topsides, to prevent the planking opening up.

Retaining the Boat's Shape   This is a very real problem. If you are converting an open boat, such as a ship's lifeboat, and the work entails removing thwarts, it would be as well to fit stays across the boat at gunwale level. Start by fitting two eye plates to the inside of the gunwales with bolts, then put a chain across the boat and tighten it with a rigging screw. Two such stays should be enough. In addition to this you should fit legs amidships. The method is to fit shores at two or three places along the side, not fastening them directly to the side of the boat but fitting them under a piece of timber that is screwed to the ship. This enables one to remove and replace shores during repairs if they should prove to be in the way.

During major rebuildings of old yachts or decked fishing boats, if frames and floors are to be replaced, you may need cross bracing. If a keel has to be replaced, temporary bilge keels, combined with new frames and floors, are one way of keeping the vessel's shape.

In *Boadicea* (an 1808 30ft Maldon smack), before her new keel was fitted, the owner cut and fitted six temporary frames and two 12ft bilge keels. This was a policy of perfection!

Workbench If you are working away from a boatyard, you will need something to work on. A possible substitute for a workbench is a heavy 3in plank, 12in wide, which could be laid along the thwarts of an open boat, or on trestles alongside. You will have to fix a substantial vice, at least 8in across, to this plank, and you will also need a bench hook for supporting planks or timbers when you are cutting a tenon or doing any other small piece of work on the bench. In addition, you will need a solidly built trestle to act as a saw horse.

3
Tools

Shipwrights use most of the tools that joiners and cabinet-makers use, and the following notes may be of some help. To begin with, never buy cheap tools; always go for the best quality.

Ordinary Carpentry Tools

Chisels and Gouges Like cut-throat razors, some chisels hold their edges well; others do not. Probably the best chisels come from Japan, where a long tradition of making Samurai swords has produced the finest cutting steel in the world.

Always use a mallet when striking a chisel, and always hold a small chisel near the point and not by the handle when hitting it. This rule must be followed when cutting a mortice. Larger chisels, when used for less precise work, can be held by the handle.

Gouges are particularly useful for cutting out the recesses for bolt heads.

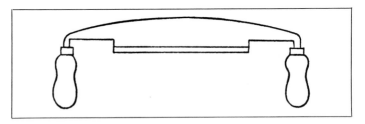

Drawknife used for shaping spars

Drawknives and Spokeshaves These are both useful tools. The former are used for trimming off large slivers of timber, the latter for finer work. Drawknives are much used by spar-makers. Spokeshaves can be used in places too small or too awkward for the use of the smallest plane.

Hammers, Mauls, Sledges and Mallets Hammers should be of good-quality cast steel, otherwise they will chip and become pitted with use. They vary in size from the small cross-pein hammers of about 2oz to the ball-pein hammers of about 2lb, which would be used for driving a 6-gauge nail.

Hammers used for clenching rooves should not exceed 12oz in weight, as the 'dolly' used to back up the head of the nail needs to be about four times the weight of the hammer. It is a very exhausting business holding up a dolly of more than 3lb in weight, particularly while lying on your back under the bottom planking of the boat. The dolly can be an old flatiron, or the head of a maul or a sledgehammer.

Mauls are used for driving in large spikes. If one used a hammer for such a purpose, it would bounce off the head of a spike. The heavier sledge is used for heavier jobs, such as driving home drift bolts. A claw-headed hammer is useful for drawing nails.

A wooden mallet is essential for work with chisels. Not only does it not damage the handle of the chisel, but it will drive the chisel more accurately than a hammer.

Planes There are many sizes and types of plane, from the 'trying' plane with a sole about 3ft in length, used for dressing the surface of planks or large timbers, to the miniature block plane, which may be only $1\frac{1}{2}$in long and is used for trimming tight corners. This plane can be held in the palm of one's hand. The most useful size for the work-bench is the steel smoothing plane, such as a Stanley, about 9in long with a blade 2in wide. This plane is light enough to be used with one hand, but whenever it is possible use two hands for the job. The left hand, which guides the plane, should be placed on the knob at the forward end, or across the body of the plane, with the thumb nearest to the operator, and pressed down steadily while the right hand works the plane. When using a steel plane, keep a wax candle to hand and rub this over the surface of the plane from time to time. This will prevent the plane binding or sticking to the wood.

Rabbet planes, as their name implies, are used for cutting rabbets (or rebates) in joinery and cabinet work. A hollow-bottom (or, as it is sometimes called, hollow-and-round) plane is used for finishing work in spar-making.

Screwdrivers The screwdriver is an important tool, and one needs a different one for each size of screw used, probably ranging from $\frac{1}{8}$in to $\frac{1}{2}$in. For the heavier sizes of screw it is better to use a brace and bit, for this combination gives a better leverage and there is less chance of the screw sticking. The business end of the screwdriver should be ground flat for about $\frac{1}{8}$in and the edge should be slightly hollow ground. A massive 'London' screwdriver is an essential tool for reaching screws on which it is impossible to use a brace and bit. These big steel screwdrivers are usually made up from $1\frac{1}{4}$in by $\frac{1}{4}$in steel strip and may be anything up to 3ft long.

For speed, the 'pump' screwdriver is a most useful tool, without the disadvantages of a power-driven tool, where the screw may be left spinning in the hole, thereby destroying the holding power of the wood round it. However, with the pump type, it is advisable to harden up the screw with a normal screwdriver.

Sliding Bevel This is more flexible than the simple hinged bevel. It will be in constant use, for in boatbuilding there are hardly any right-angles.

Saws If you have access to power-driven saws, your work will be that much easier. Certainly no one today would willingly work in a saw pit, cutting planks out of a log. For rough work your hand saw should have about six teeth to the inch; for cleaner cutting you need ten to twelve teeth to the inch. You also need a small tenon saw and a keyhole saw for cutting holes in awkward places. Saws need frequent sharpening and this is not a job for an amateur. Oil helps when you are cutting hard woods.

Band Saw This is a power-driven saw used for cutting out bends or frames. The marked plank to be cut is put into position on the saw bench, the power is turned on and then the sawyer gently steers the wood round the curve. After cutting about 12in, tap a wedge into the cut to prevent it closing and so jamming the blade. This procedure

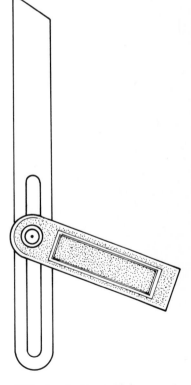

Sliding bevel with 10in blade

25

should be repeated every foot. If the saw jams, the power should immediately be turned off and the wood joggled back into position until the blade is free; sawing can then be resumed.

Pit saw This is a saw with a long slender blade similar to a length of band saw but fitted with a handle at each end. It is worked by two men, one on the top of the log to be cut and the other man below in the saw pit. The pit saw only cuts on the downward stroke.

Boring Tools Long auger bits are necessary for drilling through heavy timbers, false keels, deadwoods, etc. The auger should be well greased, as indeed should drift bolts, for which soft soap is recommended, as it does not lessen their holding power. The use of jigs is essential for accurate drilling.

Boring Holes: Jigs To bore a hole, say for a keel bolt, proceed as follows. First, draw the centre line of the bolt on the bottom of the keel. Then take two pieces of soft wood, straight on both sides, say 3in by 1in and about 15in longer than the hole to be bored. Draw a mark at right-angles to the centre line and $1\frac{1}{2}$in from the mark at the centre of the hole, and place one piece of wood in a vertical position on this mark and nail it into position; then put the other piece of wood on the other side of the keel, thus making a sandwich of it. Cramp both pieces tightly. There are now two pieces of wood cramped to the keel and projecting 15in above it. This, of course, means that the garboards have to be removed.

Take another piece of wood, this time as long as the keel is wide, and in its centre bore a hole exactly the same size as the shank of the drill that is to be used for drilling the keel-bolt hole. Cramp it between the two vertical pieces. The jig is now complete and you can start boring. Use either a hand brace or an electric drill; if you use the latter, be sure that it is a heavy-duty slow-turning machine.

Jigs for boring for keel bolts, etc:
1 and 2 Oak blocks to the thickness of the keel with pilot holes lined up
3 and 4 Side-pieces
5 Keel or any other plank on edge that has to be drilled

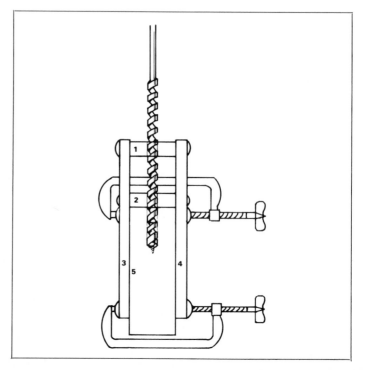

Drilling for Kelson, Keel and Deadwood In fishing boats and similar craft the keels may be no more than 4in wide, but up to 18in deep, so the drilling must be very accurate. In the stern, where the deadwood lies on top of the keel, bolts may be as much as 4ft long, though forward they may be only half this measurement.

There are two problems here. First, when the kelson is in position, it is not possible to see if the direction line of the drill is right, and, second, there may not be enough room below deck to take the drill. For the short holes forward it is better to drill through the new floors and the old keel before the kelson is fitted. After it is in place, it can be drilled from underneath through the holes already drilled in the old keel and the floors. The problem of the longer holes can be solved without too much difficulty. For the long hole through the deadwood aft, it may be necessary to drill down through the deck. The position of the hole in the deck can be arrived at by shining a torch up through the existing holes in the deadwood and marking the light spot on the underside of the deck. When drilling for drift bolts, your hole should be somewhat less than the diameter of the rod.

Jig for Boring Stern-tubes For this jig a special bit is needed – a $\frac{3}{4}$in morse drill welded accurately on to the end of a 5ft length of $\frac{3}{4}$in stainless steel rod. Obtain an 18in length of $\frac{3}{4}$in inside diameter tube, which should just fit over the $\frac{3}{4}$in rod. Weld a 3in by $\frac{3}{8}$in bolt on to the tube at each end. Take a 4ft length of 2in $\times$ 2in $\times$ $\frac{1}{4}$in angle iron, and drill two holes in it to take the $\frac{3}{8}$in bolts. The holes should be drilled on marks 1in from the corner of the angle iron.

This jig of course only provides a guide for the pilot hole. To make a hole big enough for a boring bar, you may bore a $\frac{3}{16}$in hole in the dead centre of one end of a piece of brass shaft $\frac{3}{4}$in in diameter and 2in long. Thread this on to the thread at the end of a $1\frac{1}{4}$in auger, insert it into the $\frac{3}{4}$in pilot hole and turn. Any other size of auger can of course be used.

If an auger breaks inside the hole, draw out the top part of the auger, fill the hole with pitch and plug it.

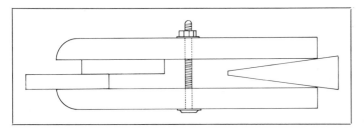

Clamp made of two pieces of hardwood connected by a screw bolt that has plenty of play. When the clamp grips the planks, it can be tightened up by driving in a wedge

Clamps (or Cramps) These serve as an extra pair of hands as well as being essential pieces of equipment for holding bent planks and timbers in position; 24in sash clamps and 6in and 3in G-clamps are all essential. A clamp can be made up from two pieces of hardwood connected by a screw bolt that has plenty of play. When the clamp grips the planks, it can be tightened by driving in a wedge.

Miscellaneous Tools Steel measuring tapes, setsquares, compasses and dividers (for scribing) and bevels are all necessary tools. A sliding bevel is an essential piece of equipment. It needs a blade 8–10in long.

Punches come in two kinds, solid and hollow. The solid punch is for countersinking nail heads and the hollow punch for driving home rooves.

Shipwrights' Tools

Broadaxe or Shipwright's Axe These axes are little used today. They were always made and used in pairs for chopping the waste timber away from deadwood, floors, etc. The reason for their being made in pairs was that the handle is offset either to the right or to the left of the blade, so that the shipwright does not bark his knuckles. The axe is used with both hands, the handle of course being offset away from the timber that is being trimmed. The ash handle is steam-bent to give the required offset.

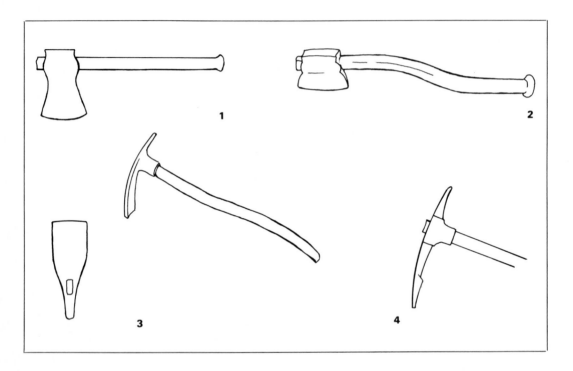

Broadaxes and adzes:
1 and 2 Side and above view of broadaxe, showing bent handle
3 Shipwrights' adze, side and end view
4 American lipped adze, side view and section

Adze There are various types of adze, but only two are of interest to boatbuilders. These are the shipwright's adze and the American 'lipped' adze. In the hands of a skilled shipwright the adze can be a very accurate tool. Even in the hands of the not so skilled it is a useful tool for clearing away waste timber from deadwoods, stemposts and sternposts, floors and timbers.

The virtue of the lipped adze is that the corners of the cutting edge are turned back, so there is no nasty scoring from an uneven cut. The adze is used in the following manner. The shipwright stands with his feet about a foot apart and square on to the work, with his right hand grasping the end of the handle and his left hand about 10in from the head. The handle is about 30in long. If the timber to be cut is about waist height, he tucks his right hand into his middle and swings the adze head up and down with the left hand; his right hand moves up and down to bring the adze head more or less flat on to the timber that is being timmed. To begin with he makes tentative light cuts, bearing in mind that two light and accurate cuts are better than a heavy cut that may have overstepped the mark.

The adze is a dangerous tool, like the axe or the pin maul, and the harder you hit with it, the more dangerous it becomes.

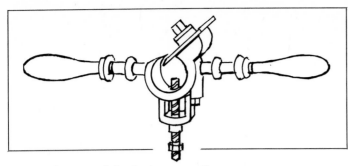

Mute This is a tool for shaping tree-nails.

Dolly A solid piece of iron or steel about 2lb in weight, this is used during the riveting of copper nails. It is held against the head of the nail, to take the weight of the hammer blows on the rivet.

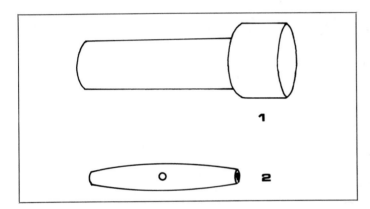

1 Dolly, turned out of $1\frac{1}{2}$in mild steel. The handle is about $1\frac{1}{8}$in thick and the end of the dolly is slightly convex
2 The centre barrel of a rigging screw makes a useful hollow punch for hardening up rooves

4

Sequence
of Work

In any major rebuild of the hull of a decked yacht or fishing boat planning the order of work is important, to avoid having to undo something you have already done. One has to look ahead, ordering timber that may not be needed for some months. The following sequence is based on Michael Frost's rebuild of *Boadicea*, a 30ft Maldon oyster smack originally built in 1808. The work described took Mr Frost three or four years. (See John Lewis, *Vintage Boats*, David & Charles, 1975).

1   Gut the inside and remove the flooring and lining from cabin and hold. Clean out thoroughly.
2   Take out loose ballast.
3   Chip out any concrete in the bottom of the boat.
4   Remove the kelson.
5   Remove the floors one at a time, and cut and fit new floors. Fix with temporary service bolts to the old keel and with flat nails to the skin.
6   Take out the old frames, again one at a time, and replace by new frames temporarily fastened to the old skin.
7   Make up 'short floors' to join the base of the frames together and fit with service bolts (fishing boats).
8   Take out the apron, forward deck beams, breasthook and knight-heads. Fit new apron.
9   Fair up the floors and short floors. Fit the kelson and fasten it to the short floors with dump bolts. If the garboards are to come out, they can be cut to allow you to cramp the kelson into position.
10   Fit the new breasthook, knightheads and first forward deck beam, and fasten.
11   Fit the shelves. The problem of getting the shelves to shape can be solved by cutting them when the timber is green and then clamping them round the *outside* of the boat. If the existing deck is to be retained, holes may have to be cut in the planking at the bows and in the transom, so that the excess lengths can project outboard until they have been drawn close to the frames and fastened down. Some cutting to fit may be necessary at the stern.
12   Before the old keel can be dropped out, the weight of the boat has to be taken up somehow. This can be done by fitting 2ft-deep temporary bilge keels 4in thick and 12ft long. These should be very accurately fitted to the old skin and fastened to three temporary frames on each side.
13   A pattern must now be made for the new keel. This can be done by offering up a $\frac{1}{4}$in-thick deal plank to the old keel and very carefully scribing, then cutting rebates round each floor. The chief reason for such care is that the keels in very old boats may be anything but straight along the top.
14   The new keel is made up from these patterns, and is placed on rollers ready to be rolled under the boat when the old keel is taken out.

15 The temporary bolts and wedges are removed from the old keel and, with only the slightest persuasion, down it should drop.

16 The new keel is now rolled into position. The rollers should be placed on planks a few inches clear of the ground to allow for car jacks to be slid underneath. When the keel is in position, it is jacked up. If there is any droop or twist, there will be still quite a lot of marking and cutting to do. The marking is done by means of a length of whipping twine laid along the top of the new keel. If the twine is not gripped at any point, it means there is a hollow that has to be evened out. When the keel has been properly trimmed up, it is then through-bolted to the new floors and the kelson.

17 The old transom and the top half of the sternpost can now be cut away, and the new transom nailed into position on the new fashion frame (which is fastened to the old skin). These planks are not cut to shape at this stage, but overlap the ship on each side. The new sternpost is not put in, nor for that matter is the old one taken out, until the new keel has been fitted.

18 The new sternpost and stempost are then fitted, and the new back-bone and framing are now complete.

19 The next stage is the planking, which begins with the garboards. When the planking is completed, the overlapping transom planks are trimmed off flush with the topside.

20 The old deck and deck beams are removed and replaced with new beams and deck planking.

21 After planking, the seams are caulked with oakum and then splined. The deck planks are likewise caulked and payed.

22 Stanchions, bulwarks and bulwark rails are fitted.

23 Hatch coamings and covers are fitted.

24 The hull is painted and varnished.

5

Timber
and Fastenings

Timber is of course the most important item in any repair on wooden boats. Types of timber in common use in boatbuilding vary from country to country and continent to continent. Most boatbuilding timber in use in the British Isles, with the exception of British oak and elm, is imported.

Timber

Burma Teak   Teak is the finest of all woods for deckhouses, hatchways and planking. It will stand sun or sea without warping or shrinking, even when it is not painted, varnished or oiled. It is hard and very durable, but it splits easily in thin boards. It must always be drilled for fastenings.

Canadian Rock Elm   This is a good durable wood, suitable for keels, floors and timbers. It lasts well under water and holds fastenings well. When used for timbers, it is liable to break at the turn of the bilge; and these breaks can sometimes appear after the boat has been built.

English Elm   Elm should not be seasoned. It should be felled in winter and used as soon after as possible. It holds fastenings well and is very durable under salt water, but it rots quickly in fresh water. If your keel is of English elm, scrub it clean and tar it before laying up for the winter. The same thing of course applies to the elm bottom strakes of punts and other flat-bottomed craft. English elm should not be used for floors, as it will rot quickly there, nor for the false keel if the boat has to lie in a mud berth and dry out between tides. Make absolutely certain the timber comes from a tree free from Dutch elm disease.

Greenheart   This is a very hard timber, so tough that nails cannot be driven into it. It can be used for bottom planking, keels and rudders, for it is teredo-resistant. It will not bend easily. It should be cut when green, for a seasoned log will blunt any saw blade almost instantly. Greenheart is also used for fairleads, belaying pins and for any place on a boat's deck where there is liable to be chafe – for instance, on the foredecks to take the wear and tear of the anchor and chains. Greenheart is very heavy, much heavier than either teak or oak and it will not float in seawater. Its dust and splinters are poisonous, so take care when using it.

Hackmatack (Tamarack or American Larch)   This is a durable, rot-resistant and tough wood, used for floor timbers and frames because of its grown crooks, which are cut from where the trunk meets the major roots at ground level.

Iroko A tough knot-free hardwood, this can be bought in wide planks. When freshly sawn, it is a banana colour, but after exposure to sunlight, it darkens to a grey-brown. It holds fastenings well and is excellent for topside planking, the sides of cabin trunks, coamings, etc.

Larch This is a good timber for planking, lasts very well and is reasonably tough. It was normally used for the planking of ships' lifeboats.

Locust Not available in Europe but widely used on the north-east coast of the USA, locust is heavier than oak and even tougher. It is also rot-resistant, but like greenheart is difficult to work. It is used for any part of a boat where both toughness and strength are needed.

Mahogany Most so-called mahogany comes from West Africa. Only a few of these mahoganies are suitable for planking. They are often not fully seasoned, so may warp and shrink. The best mahogany comes from Honduras. It has a very long life and holds fastenings well, except for iron fastenings, which soon rot the wood. It is a beautiful wood for cabin fittings, etc.

Oak Seasoned autumn-cut English oak is one of the best woods for boatbuilding, particularly for framing, including beams and floors. It lasts well and holds fastenings well. The autumn felling is important, for if there is any sap in the wood, it will soon rot. Oak needs to season for several years before use.

Oak, American White and Red In colonial days the Admiralty put an embargo on the use of American oak in British frigates, claiming that it was not as long-lasting or as rot-resistant as seasoned British oak. Whatever the truth of this, white oak is held in high esteem by American boatbuilders for all structural timbers. When steaming frames and other timbers, it is best to use freshly felled trees. Red oak is more absorbent and softer than white oak, and much more subject to rot. It is very much a second best, but is used in commercial craft.

Pitch Pine This highly resinous, tough wood is very suitable for planking, particularly below the waterline. It is resistant to rot, has a very long life and is excellent for carlines and stringers. Its disadvantage for topside planking is that it tends to 'weep' resin, and the seams between the planks of pitch pine will always show.

Sitka Spruce This is a softwood that is very light, and is far the best wood for spars. For this purpose it should be bought in the form of undressed poles, that is, with the bark still on the wood. These poles should be picked for their straightness, resilience and even spacing of knots. When stripped with a draw knife, they will soon dry and become much lighter. Spruce bruises easily, particularly in the way of the gaff jaws, so masts should be given some protection at this point. Spruce is also an ideal timber for dinghies and prams that have to be lifted inboard.

White Pine Widely used in boatbuilding on the coast of Maine in the USA because of its cheapness and availability, it absorbs water more readily than larch or cedar, but is less brittle than the latter. It is best used for bulkheads, bunk frames and other interior work. Suitable also for punts and dories.

Yellow Pine (Southern or Longleaf Pine) This is comparable to pitch pine (it is sometimes so-called) and shares the virtues and defects of pitch pine. It is longer-lasting than American white oak and can be used with iron or galvanised steel fastenings without danger of rot. Use as for pitch pine.

Fastenings

In boat work, drill for all fastenings. Copper, monel metal or naval brass are normally used in good-quality work, though galvanised steel nails are also used. Swedish iron nails are longer-lasting than steel, but difficult to obtain. For heavier work on large craft, tree-nails (trunnels) may be used.

Copper Nails and Rivets They are the normal method in yacht-building in Europe for fastening planks to timbers in both clinker and carvel planking. After drilling, the nails are driven through planking and timber; and then the roove, which is a small washer and is always a very tight fit, is driven home to the timber by means of a hollow punch. The nail is then cut off with a pair of pincers, leaving enough metal to form a head, which will be burred over the roove with the rounded end of a ball-pein hammer. Alternatively, the nails may be clench-fastened. The rooves are usually omitted, the nails being turned over and hammered flat across the grain of the timber.

The size of copper nails is indicated by a gauge number. The higher the number, the smaller the gauge of nail. As a rough guide, nails from $\frac{3}{4}$in to $1\frac{1}{2}$in long would be 13 or 12 gauge, those between $1\frac{3}{4}$in and 3in 10 gauge, from 3in to 5in 8 gauge and from 6in to 12in 6 gauge.

For heavier work, such as planking a 30ft fishing boat, 4in flat-point iron or galvanised steel nails would be used. Iron is better than steel and monel metal is better still. Alternatively, bronze holdfast nails, in common use in the USA, will make a strong fastening.

Withdrawing Old Fastenings When fastenings have not corroded away entirely but are stuck fast to the frames, they must be cut with a hacksaw and driven out through the planking. The holes must then be plugged and dowelled, the dowels being set in epoxy resin.

Fastening Planked Decks If the deck is tongue- and groove-planked, it should be either screwed or nailed to the deck beams. For decks without much camber, the planks can be ship-lapped and nail- and roove-fastened at the laps. For ordinary and heavier deck planking ($1\frac{1}{2}$in–2in thick) the planks should be 'secret' fastened. That is, the planks are edge-fastened between the frames, either by bronze pins or galvanised nails. In the latter case ordinary 2in round-headed nails are used. They are hammered into the side of one plank, 1in deep, the heads are cut off and the next plank is then hammered hard up against the plank with the projecting nails. For the bronze pins it would be necessary to drill both planks, which needs accurate aligning, or the deck planks could be screwed to the deck beams and the screwholes plugged with dowels.

Screws These are used for various purposes in boat work. In the USA bronze screws are normally used for planking, in place of copper nails and rivets. Otherwise screws are used for hoodends, where the forward ends of the planking are fastened to the stempost and the after ends to the transom. Flat-head screws are the ones most commonly used.

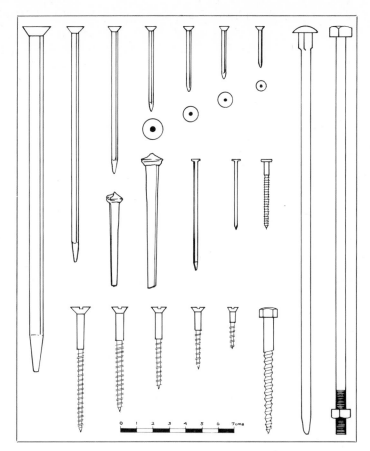

Fastenings:
Top: Copper boat nails ranging in size from 210mm to 25mm and copper rooves for the smaller sizes. *Centre:* galvanised steel boat nails, 55mm and 80mm flat points, 67mm boat nail and 42mm wire nail. *Centre right:* 42mm monel metal holdfast (or anchorfast) nail. *Bottom:* phosphor bronze or Everdur (96 per cent copper, 4 per cent silicon) flat-headed screws ranging in size from 75mm to 25mm. *Bottom right:* 245mm monel metal drift and keel bolts

Top: Copper nails and rivets:
1 Dolly (A) held against head of nail while a hollow punch (B) is driving the rivet home
2 The point of the nail is snipped off
3 Enough is left to be burred over the rivet, by means of a ball-pein hammer, while the dolly is held against the head of the nail
Below: Deck fastenings:
Left: side fastenings, with galvanised steel nails driven into the deck beam.
Right: method of secret fastening. Note annular rings in the deck planks are facing downwards

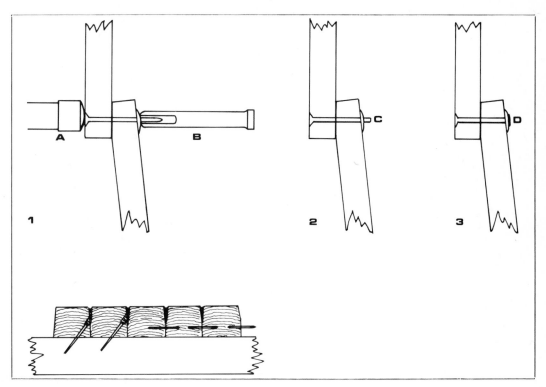

Screws are made of galvanised steel, brass or naval bronze, in sizes from 4 gauge ($\frac{1}{2}$in long) to 16 gauge (4in long). A rule of thumb is that screws should be three times as long as the thickness of the plank to be fastened. For instance, to fasten $\frac{1}{2}$in-thick clinker larch planking to an oak stem, 10 gauge screws 1$\frac{1}{2}$in long would be used. When drilling, three different sizes of drill have to be used for each hole. The largest would be for countersinking the head; the next would be for drilling through the planking, allowing sufficient freedom for the screw to be turned by hand; the smallest drill will be used to bore the hole in the timber (in this case the oak stempost) to which the plank is to be fastened. The resulting hole in the timber will allow the screw to be turned easily under firm pressure. Petroleum jelly (vaseline) on the thread of the screw greatly eases the passage of the screw into the hard wood, and has some preservative value.

In boring for the countersinking for the screw head the depth of the plug should be two-thirds its diameter. The plugs, which will be made from the same wood as the planking, are glued into position with the grain running in the same direction as the plank. The plugs should be made long enough to project about $\frac{1}{4}$in when glued and set in position; they can then be trimmed flush with a chisel.

Tree-nails (or Trunnels)   These are in some ways the most durable of all fastenings. The reason the hull of the seventeenth-century Swedish warship *Wasa* held together after more than 200 years at the bottom of Stockholm harbour was that she was largely fastened by tree-nails. Tree-nails are not much used in modern boatbuilding practice, except for such jobs as fastening the deadwood to the keel. They can be any size from $\frac{3}{8}$in to 1$\frac{1}{2}$in diameter. They are cut from seasoned cleft oak, and well dried before being driven home; they are cleft because the grain will run truly for the whole length of the tree-nail. They are made to be a good driving fit. Like the plugs, they are cut off flush with a chisel, then split at right-angles to the grain of the plank or timber they are fastening, and a small wedge is driven in hard. Shipwrights carry a tool called a mute for making tree-nails. The snag with them is that, to be effective, they require a very tight and accurate fit between the pieces of timber that have to be fastened together.

Bolts   These are used for through-fastening keels to floors, aprons to stemposts, etc. They have a head at one end and a nut and washer at the other end, which is of course threaded. They are made of iron, galvanised steel, bronze or monel metal. The choice of metal for bolts depends on the fastenings in the rest of the vessel. For keel bolts in a cast-iron ballast keel or cast-lead keel iron is more practical than steel. These bolts need to be made red hot and then dipped in black varnish.

Drift bolts   These are long fastenings, which have a tapered end and no thread, and dispense with any nut. They are used in the keel and for joining up heavy stem and stern timbers, etc. The holes for drift bolts are drilled with augers, and when edge-boring planks it is advisable to use a jig. Drift bolts are tapered by hammering on an anvil, without heating; and a taper of less than an inch is enough.

Performance of Different Materials in Fastenings   *Monel metal* is an alloy made of 70 per cent nickel and 30 per cent copper, and highly resistant to corrosion from seawater, even if in contact with iron or steel. It is the only metal suitable for fastening stainless-steel fittings below the waterline. It is difficult to work, but, if properly heat-treated, can be forged satisfactorily. It is very expensive.

When using monel metal for fastenings in hardwood such as oak or greenheart, drill the holes to the depth of the nails. This is no way affects their holding power. To avoid bending the nails, use a punch instead of hitting them direct. The heads of all fastenings, nails or screws, should be countersunk and covered with wooden plugs cold-glued into position. The plugs should be made of the same wood as the planking.

Silicon bronze is probably the next best fastening for use anywhere in the boat. It is greatly superior to brass, which corrodes by dezincification in seawater.

Copper fastenings (nails and rivets) tend to remain sound.

Stainless steel is suitable only for interior fittings and for use on fresh-water craft. The durability of stainless steel depends apparently on a protective film of oxide; when not exposed to the oxygen in the air, stainless-steel bolts and fastenings soon lose their protective film and then corrode as rapidly as mild steel.

Naval brass suffers less corrosion from seawater than ordinary brass.

Hot-dip galvanised steel is the most economical fastening, but as soon as the zinc surface goes, the steel rusts quickly.

Swedish iron, which is difficult to obtain, makes a better-lasting fastening than steel, but causes rot in mahogany and slight surface rot in oak.

Yellow metal is sometimes used for keel bolts and stem and stern assemblies, but it crystallises away more quickly than iron or even galvanized-steel bolts.

Tree-nails are in some ways the most durable of fastenings. (See the magazine *Practical Boat Owner*, check card, 3rd series, no 8, which was compiled from information supplied by the GKN fasteners-corrosion laboratory.)

Use of Tie Rods Bronze tie rods $\frac{3}{16}$ in in diameter are used to help retain the shape of the side decks between the carlines of the cockpit or cabin and the shelf or gunwale. They are threaded at each end and held with nuts and washers outside the shelves or gunwales and inside the carlines.

Tie rods are also used fore and aft between deck beams, particularly between the mast partners (the beams fore and aft of the mast step). The addition of tie rods in the restoration of old craft can be of considerable help in preserving their shape.

The strength of metal fittings on spars and decks is no greater than their fastenings; so, whenever possible, use through-bolts in addition to screws. This particularly applies to shroud fastenings on masts. Chain plates should always be through-bolted to a doubling piece inside the planking.

PART
TWO
Repairs
and Replacements

6

Keels
Stems and Sterns

To remove the keel from an old vessel is a daunting operation. If the keel is rotten, the odds are the garboards and some of the floors may also be decayed. With the removal of the garboards, the drawing of the keelbolts from the apron, kelson and floors, and the cutting of the lap joints fore and aft, the keel should be free to drop out. If this is allowed to happen, there is a real danger of the vessel going out of shape and even becoming hopelessly hogged. The hull must be given some positive support, from temporary bilge keels at least as long as one-third of the overall length of the hull. These temporary keels will have to be bolted to the frames or to temporary frames fitted for this purpose. When in position, these bilge keels should be jacked up, and heavy chocks (old railway sleepers would do) placed underneath them. The weight of the boat is now taken on the bilge keels.

In addition to this, a rough cradle should be fixed under bow and stern to prevent any sag. To complete the straitjacket, fix two chains with rigging screws on the fore and aft line, one set up on deck from the stempost to the sternpost and one inside from the fore foot to the after end of the kelson. This complicated procedure works. It was the method used by Michael Frost for replacing *Boadicea's* keel (see p 87).

When the new keel has been bolted into position, the keel bolts should be countersunk at least $\frac{3}{4}$in and the holes plugged. A galvanised-iron shoe (or keelband) can then be fitted with galvanised-iron screws for fastening.

The Kelson The repair or replacement of a kelson is relatively easy. The kelson normally lies inside the boat on top of floors and frames, and is through-bolted to the keel. Once these bolts are freed, the kelson can be lifted. In a decked craft it is almost an impossibility to replace a damaged or rotten kelson with a new kelson in one piece without taking the deck off, unless a hole is made in the planking or the transom, so that the new kelson can be pushed inboard. The alternative is to make it up from two or three pieces, joined with hook scarphs.

Masts are frequently stepped on the kelson. This is the first point to look at for decay. If the kelson has decayed here and only here, the best thing is to cut it some 3ft aft of the mast step, remove the kelson forward of that point and scarph in a new length. If there is rot here, the pressure by the mast on this inadequate support will probably have forced the garboards out just below this point, causing them to leak.

If the new length of kelson can be made to overlap the apron, so that it can be through-bolted to the keel, you will achieve a very strong structure. The mast step should be of oak, liberally coated with fungicide and fastened to the kelson with coach screws. It should be bedded down with white lead paint.

If the kelson has to be bent at the after end, it will have to be steamed. It can then be chocked or cramped into position, to allow the curve to set. After that the tops of the floors may have to be faired off, so that it lies truly. When that has been done, the kelson should be coated with Cuprinol and either given a coat of bitumen or bedded in white lead.

Frames and Floors If a boat has to be reframed and refloored throughout, a sensible method is to work in 2ft- or 3ft-wide sections, starting at the bow. First strip out the rotten timbers in the first of these sections, drive out the fastenings, clean up the inside of the planking, remove any butt pads and plug the nail holes. Coat the whole area with Cuprinol or some other fungicide, and fit and clamp the new timbers into position.

John Milgate, a professional boatbuilder, fitting new grown-oak sister frames to the hull of the fishing boat *Charlotte Ellen (Keith Mirams)*

If any of the planking has to be replaced, you can treat it roughly. For instance, slots can be cut in it, so that you can get a proper hold for the clamps. Otherwise timbers can be forced into position by means of lengths of timber chocked up against the deck head, the keel or the kelson.

To preserve the new frames and floors, coat with fungicide. If they are heavy cut frames, drill a $\frac{1}{2}$in diameter hole 6in deep into the top of the frame, fill up with linseed oil and then plug. The theory is that the oil slowly seeps down through the grain of the wood and prevents rot. An alternative is to fill the hole with Cuprinol or Woodtreat.

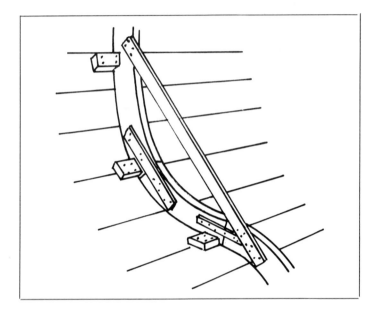

Pattern for new frame, with stops (small blocks of wood) fastened to the planking to keep pattern vertical while it is being offered up

In large craft it is quite a job removing heavy timbers. If it is impossible to knock out the bolts, special iron-cutting saws have to be used, slipped in between timber and planking. Tree-nails are easy to cut and are no problem. With copper-rooved fastenings, the burred end of the nail is removed by drilling, the roove is lifted off and the fastening is driven out by means of a hammer and punch. Sometimes a frame or a floor may be in such a rotten condition that it can be split with a chisel round the fastenings, and taken out in pieces. If the frame is going to be broken up in this way, it is as well to take patterns (or templates). These patterns can be made up of short lengths of hardboard or thin $\frac{1}{4}$in cedar planking. To make certain that the patterns are correctly placed, and lying flush with the floor and close to the planking, fasten a number of small square blocks of wood to the planks at 15in intervals in a vertical line. The pattern is then offered up against these stops until it fits snugly. The angles of the bevels should be marked on these templates, by means of a carpenter's sliding bevel. The line of the fitting surface would then be transferred to the oak crook, to avoid sapwood or any flaws. The rest of the dimensions would be transferred and the table of the saw bench set to the angle of the bevel. The frame would be finished by hand with adze and plane.

There are various ways of making frames. They are usually steam-bent or fashioned from large grown crooks. When the latter cannot be obtained, an alternative method is to double up the frames from say two or three straight 2in-thick planks (if the original frames were 4in-sided).

42

Each half of the frame is cut from three pieces of the 2in plank, scarphed together. Another and extremely strong method is to cut $\frac{3}{4}$in marine ply to shape and to side-laminate five or six pieces to make up the thickness of the old frame.

When offering up the new frames or floors, chalk the planking quite heavily. Only when the chalk has rubbed off the whole face is the new frame ready for fitting. Before finally fitting, drill holes for the new fastenings through the planking from inside. A matchstick pushed through each hole makes it easier to see on the outside.

Cutting frames from grown crooks for a craft as large as a fishing

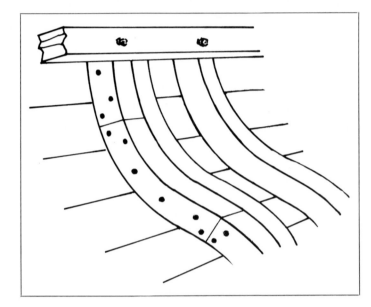

Doubling up frames, by means of short lengths of straight-grained timber cut to shape, with butt joints. These sister frames are side-bolted to existing frames

smack is no light job. Done by hand, it is quite a formidable undertaking; and there are other difficulties. If the deck and shelf are not being replaced, it is a practical impossibility to fit a full-sized frame that reaches from the keel to the deckhead; so one either has to make them in two pieces, scarphed together and the scarphs fastened and glued *after* they are in position, or in one piece with the frame falling short of the keel by 3–4in. In this case it is advisable to join the feet of each pair of frames by means of a short floor, or to side-bolt them to adjacent floors.

For small craft with complicated curves, frames can be laminated (like a tennis racket). Their laminations being sprung into position and then glued and cramped.

For steamed frames, you need both a steam box and a jig for bending the frames to the right shape.

Timbers Steamed timbers (or, as they are sometimes wrongly called, ribs) can break anywhere in a boat, but they mostly break along the turn of the bilge. If several timbers are broken but the boat is still in fairly good condition in other respects, it is probably worthwhile removing the old timbers and putting new ones in their place. They can be cut and split off, and the nails cut and removed. If the old timber went up behind the gunwale or shelf, some difficulty will be experienced in removing the fastenings. However, if the old timber can be split off the nail and removed, the nail can be cut with a hacksaw blade and the

43

Steamboxes. A 10-gallon oil drum with 6in of water in it, heated over a fire and connected to a box 12ft long, 12in wide and 9in deep with a rubber hose. *Below:* a steel barrel, or cast-iron drainpipe of 4in diameter half filled with boiling water. It is plugged at the near end and kept boiling by means of a small fire below it

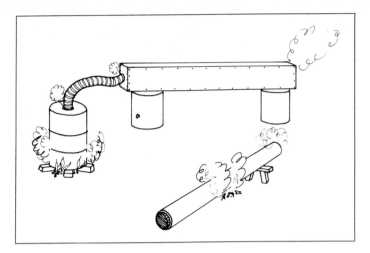

two halves prized out far enough for the ends to be gripped with nippers.

Having removed the broken timber, give the planking a good scraping down, treat it with fungicide and give it a coat of lead paint. With all the old timbers removed, the new ones can then be prepared. Use good-quality English or American white oak or Canadian rock elm for the job, and be sure that the wood is dry and straight-grained. It may be impossible without taking the boat to pieces to put new timbers back in one length, so either scarph across the hog or allow them to pass each other and go up the other side for about three planks. Where the boat is in such condition that it is not worthwhile, or definitely inadvisable, to remove the broken timbers, they can be doubled, either along their whole length or just a foot or two either side of the break. When you double the timbers along the turn of the bilge, you will find it inadvisable sometimes to push them right down to the planking just where the old ones are broken, and better to allow them to take an easier curve. Fasten all the lands up and clench them, but do not try to put a nail into the plank where the timber leaves it; instead fit a wooden wedge-shaped piece under the timber and then fasten through to that.

Steaming When there is an amount of steaming to do, it probably pays to make a proper steambox. This should be about 12ft long, 12in wide and 9in deep, and made of $\frac{3}{4}$in plywood shuttering, which is excellent for the job and not too expensive. Any 10-gallon drum will do for holding the water, 6in being enough. The drum is connected to the steambox by rubber hose, and it should be heated with a blowlamp or Calor gas to bring it to the boil.

Do not put the timber in until there is plenty of steam and the box feels warm to the touch. Then allow one hour of steaming for every inch of thickness of timber that is to be steamed. If there are only a few timbers to steam, it is not worth making a box. A piece of steel barrel or drainpipe about 4in diameter and plugged at one end will do. Place one end on a stool and half fill with water. Build a small fire beneath the water, which will soon boil. Place the timbers in the boiling water, and if they are too short, tie a piece of string to one end and keep the other end with you. About half an hour's boil is about right for timbers $\frac{1}{2}$in thick.

The steamed timbers should be put into the boat while still wet, and cramped and fastened immediately.

A jig for bending frames can be made from a 2in-thick oak plank,

44

with 1in diameter steel rods set along whatever curve is needed (taken from a pattern or the old frames). The two ends of the freshly steamed timber are held together by a wooden strap.

Laminating If one uses modern resin glues, laminating any curved timber of a vessel should be quite satisfactory. On a boat with long overhangs, and consequently a long stem, laminating is often the only solution. It is also useful for such parts of a vessel as knees, curved transoms, aprons and deadwoods. Before starting to laminate, select the timber with great care to make sure it is free from damp, knots and blemishes.

Having put the timber through the planing machine to the right thickness, plane each plank by hand to remove any marks left by the machine. Finally rub each piece down with coarse sandpaper to roughen the surface up a little and give the glue a key on which it can bite. The jig, which should have been prepared beforehand, can be one of several sorts. For the stem of a fishing smack, say 4in-sided and 8in-moulded, a pattern should be made from the inside of the old stem. From this pattern the jig is made by bolting blocks 4in thick on to a board of 1in-thick plywood. Now apply glue to all the laminates and place them on the jig ready for bending. It is a good idea to place additional pieces of timber the same size as the laminates inside and outside the stempiece, as these then take the marks left by the toes of the cramps and the wooden blocks. Start cramping the laminates up to the jig, beginning at the middle and working out to the ends. Where a heavy deadwood with a dozen or more laminates is to be made, a special jig is called for.

Jigs for laminating:
1 and 2 Curved former, made up of three laminates (B) fastened to 4in × 2in frames
(A) Cross member with slight convex curve on lower surface
(B) The laminates fastened to frames
(C) ½in bolts. The laminates are held down by the cross member and G-clamps
(D) 4in × 2in frames
(E) 12in wide × 4in thick base board
Below: Blocks pinned down on to 1in plywood base board. This is for bending lightweight timbers

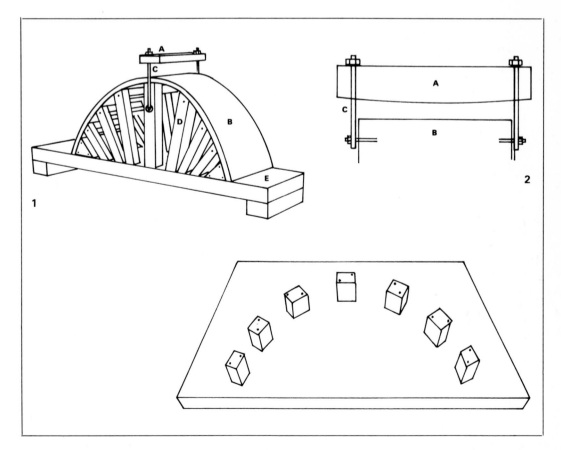

Stems, Stemposts and Aprons In replacing a large curved stempost it may be impossible to find suitable grown crooks. One solution is to make up the new stempost from two or three straight-grained timbers scarphed together. Another is to laminate it from hardwood planks that have been steamed.

The same problems apply, though to a lesser degree, with the apron. If these large timbers are cut from grown crooks, the line of the cuts presents something of a problem. The first thing is to saw the inboard face of the apron, to match the templates. The sides can then be trimmed with an adze. It may be necessary to fix up sheerlegs and a block and tackle to lift these heavy pieces of wood. To do this, fit eye bolts into the top and bottom of the apron. To move it fore and aft inside the boat, fix an additional tackle to one of the deck beams.

To make sure of a good fit, freely chalk the inside of the stempost. This chalk will rub off on any high spots on the apron. As soon as it fits precisely, first coat the fitting surfaces with Cuprinol, then either paint or coat them with bitumen. Drill through the stempost and bolt firmly into position.

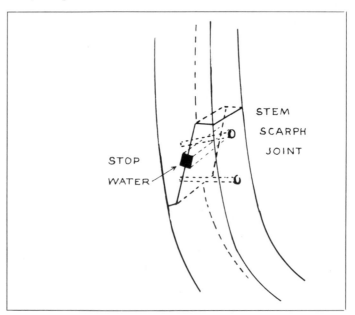

Stem scarph joint with rectangular stopwater dowel

The replacement of a stempost is a fairly straightforward operation. If the hoodends of the planking are badly worn, the simplest solution is to cut off the frayed ends of the planks and to fasten them either to the apron or to a new inner stempost, so that the plank ends are flush with the front. A new outer stempost is then fitted, wide enough to cover the front ends of the planking. This does away with the need to cut rabbets to receive the ends of the planks.

Transom and Pointed Sterns, and Counters Old vessels with either pointed sterns (like lifeboats), or transom sterns and outboard rudders that are supported by gudgeons and pintles, are a much simpler pro-position to repair than are counters with inboard rudders and rudder trunks. The latter are often a cause of rot – in such American East Coast boats as the pretty little Friendship sloops they are an invariable breeding ground for fungal decay. Such a wooden trunk should be replaced with a bronze rudder shaft set inside a bronze tube. This is an engineering

46

John Milgate at his boatyard at Peldon, working on the counter of the *Charlotte Ellen*, built in 1909 at Brightlingsea and owned by Mr J. S. Rigby. He is working with an adze in the traditional manner, astride his work (*Keith Mirams*)

job, and, unless you have experience of this sort of thing, calls for expert assistance. Sternposts are also often rotten in the way of the rudder trunk.

If the frames have gone in the counter, it will be necessary to remove some of the deck planking. Take out the old timbers and, if the curves are very acute, laminate the new frames. Steam and spring each lamination into position, gluing and clamping or chocking. With unlaminated frames, where the curves are greatest, a single sawcut inside the curve will help to stop it fracturing.

Transoms are usually made up of heavy ($2\frac{1}{2}$in-thick) planks. These are fastened together with drift bolts, but should be grooved and filleted. If the transom is made of larch, the fillets should be of oak or other hardwood. Monel metal or bronze dump bolts ($\frac{1}{2}$in) are driven down through the edges of the planks, which should be drilled at 6in intervals to within a few inches of the bottom. Before driving the bolts home, drill small holes up through the bottom plank into the bottom

John Milgate showing a different method of handling an adze, where a side approach is necessary (*Keith Mirams*)

of the bolt holes, to let the air out when the dump bolts are driven home. If this is not done, you may burst the planks. The transom is fastened to the sternpost with through-bolts.

Transoms at the end of the counter, such as those in Friendship sloops, are first framed and then planked with much lighter planking. Such transoms are nearly always curved – for strength, not looks.

Once they become old, boats with pointed sterns, such as lifeboats and Scandinavian craft, usually lose their hoodends – the screws that fasten the ends of the planks to the sternposts. It may be sufficient to drill out the dezincified brass screws and refasten with bronze or monel metal screws, but if the ends of the planks have gone, more drastic action is needed. The sternpost may have to be moved or cut, as for stemposts, and a new false sternpost fitted to cover the plank ends.

In transom-sterned boats with sound transoms but corroded hood-ends it may be possible to fit a fashion frame inside the transom and refasten the planks to that. More often than not it may be advisable to dismantle the stern, trim the planking back to clear the old hoodends, fit a new transom and refasten.

Sternposts are usually tenoned into the keel, and bolted to the dead-wood and to the inside of the transom. In some old fishing boats the sternpost is fastened outside the transom.

In old craft, such as fishing smacks or yachts, which have rotten timbers in the counter the most simple treatment may be to shorten the counter. This may be in no way detrimental to the looks of an old boat. After removing the deck planks, saw through the timbers and topside planking. Obviously some rake should be given to the sawn-off counter, though the forward sloping rake of counters on modern yachts would hardly be appropriate.

A new transom, either framed with light planking or from solid timber, will then be fitted to new fashion frames inside the planking. After the transom is fitted and the hoodends fastened, the planking can be cut off flush with the after side of the transom.

Sternposts and Deadwoods Sternposts inside counters may often need replacing, as of course will the rudder trunk. There is no simple solution to this. The after end of the boat just has to be dismantled.

7
Repairs to Planking
Decks and Rudders

Planking

Clinker or Lapstrake Planking Before one can repair anything, it is as well to know how it is constructed. The diagram should make this clearer than any written explanation. The basic difference between clinker planking and carvel planking is that clinker planks overlap and are fastened together and carvel planks abut one another. In clinker-built small craft the timbers only act as straps, helping to hold the craft together. In larger craft the heavier grown frames normally used help to retain the shape of the vessel.

Clinker planking is nowadays fastened with copper nails riveted over copper washers or rooves, or it is fastened with bronze holdfast nails or bronze screws. The planking in old fishing boats was usually iron-spiked; it often shows signs of wear along the lands, and splitting

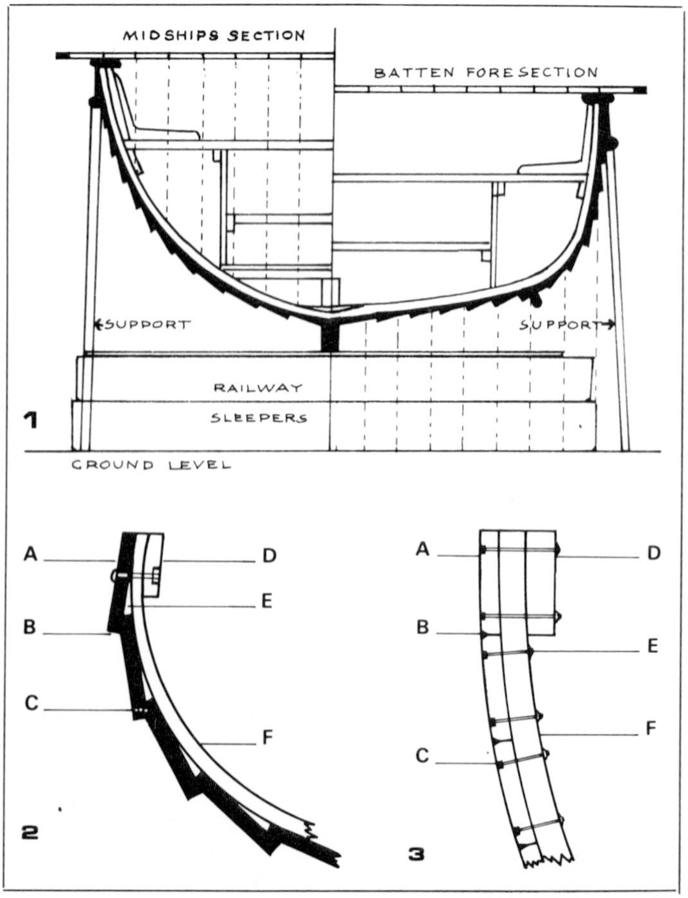

Clinker or lapstrake planking:
1 Section through clinker-built lifeboat hull
2 Details of clinker planking:
(A) Top strake, through-bolted to gunwale
(B) Land. The amount of lap varies from ¾in on dinghies to about 1½in on a 30ft lifeboat
(C) Brow. The amount of bevel taken off the top edge of the plank, so that the next plank rests flush against it
(D) Gunwale
(E) Wedge behind timber
(F) Steamed timber
3 Carvel planking:
(A) Countersunk head of copper nail, fastened through plank, timber and shelf
(B) Caulked seam
(C) Countersunk head of copper nail, fastened through plank and timber
(D & E) Copper nails bowed over roove
(F) Steamed frame

MIDSHIPS SECTION

BATTEN FORE SECTION

SUPPORT   SUPPORT

RAILWAY
SLEEPERS

1

GROUND LEVEL

A — D
        E
B —

C —
        F

2

A — D

B — E

        F
C —

3

along the line of the fastenings. If the boat is as small as a dinghy, turn it upside down, or at least list it over as far as possible, and clean off the surface with a scraper, so that the area of damage can be seen more easily. Decide what area of planking needs to be cut out and mark it with chalk. If three or four adjoining planks are damaged, remove sufficient lengths of each plank so that the scarphs are not in line.

To cut a scarph in a plank which is part of a boat (and not on the workbench) bore a $\frac{1}{4}$in-diameter hole next to the chalk line, insert a keyhole saw (or pad saw) and cut the plank. This cutting can be finished on the outside with a tenon saw and inside with a sharp chisel. To remove the damaged planking you will have to cut the fastenings. For this purpose you will find a thin-bladed chisel ($\frac{1}{16}$in thick, 1in wide and 6in long) a useful tool. You insert it between the planks, opposite a nail, and gently tap it until it comes up against the nail; then give it a sharp tap, which should cut the nail. After one or two nails have been cut, it becomes easier to insert the blade between the planks. When all fastenings at both sides of the plank have been cut, draw out the cut nails from the timbers. It does not matter about the other halves of the nails; they can be left in the damaged plank, which can be extracted, if possible in one piece, for use as an exact pattern for the new length of plank.

If it is too difficult, perhaps because the planks are too badly split, to cut the nails in this way, I suggest the following method. Working from inside the boat, drive with a centre punch a dimple into the end of the

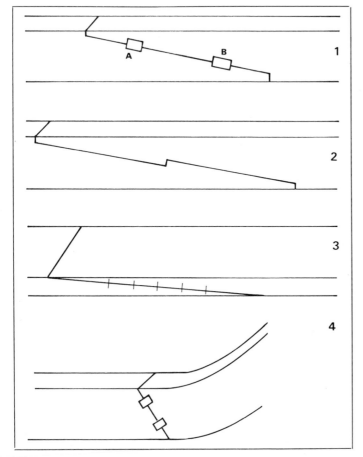

Scarphs and butt joints:
1 Common scarph with tabling (A and B)
2 Hook scarph
3 Plank scarph with feather edge, showing five registration marks
4 Butt joint between keel and stem, which is glued and dowelled

nail, in the centre of the roove. Then, using an $\frac{1}{8}$in bit in an electric drill, carefully bore the burred end of the nail off the top of the roove. With the clench removed, the roove can be lifted by means of a spike, and the nail knocked out with a pin punch.

Scarphs   The next thing is to cut the scarph, whose length should be about eight times the thickness of the plank. The scarph will be cut to a feather edge with a sharp chisel and if possible a small plane, and care should be taken that it has a perfectly flat surface both lengthways and across.

The new plank is cut to match the damaged one, plus the length either end of the two scarphs. It is a relatively simple matter cutting the scarphs in this plank, because it can be done on the bench, first by sawing and then by using a long plane. If you were cutting a number of scarphs, it would be worthwhile making a simple jig – from a 2in plank slightly wider than the plank to be scarphed and two $\frac{3}{4}$in-thick oak side-pieces acting as guides for the plane. These side-pieces, which need to be 3–4in deep, must have true straight edges. Each side-piece must be marked, say, 8in from the end, and the plank must have its ends cut off square; the side-pieces can then be nailed to it, making an angle of 5° with the 8in marks coinciding with the end of the plank. The jig can then be mounted between two sawing benches and nailed to them so that it will not move. The planks to be scarphed can first have their scarphs cut to the approximate angle with a rip saw, and then be clamped into position on the jig. They can now be planed down to the exact angle of the scarph. When both planks are completed, they can be glued up, using cramps.

If the damaged plank runs up to the stem or the transom or sternpost, it will be found that there is a slight difference to the land, which runs for about 12in in a wedge form from the stempost or transom in a feather edge to the full thickness of the land, so permitting the next plank to lie flush in the rabbet. Care must be taken to ensure that all the bevels on the plank edges are the same as on the damaged plank that has been taken out. If they are not, the plank may split when the fastenings are driven home.

When the new plank is fitted, the surfaces of the scarphs should be coated with a resorcin resin glue such as Cascophen, which is both waterproof and durable. As it is probably impossible to clamp these scarphs, they must be closely clench-fastened immediately after they have been coated with glue and placed in position.

If you are faced with the problem of fitting new planking to cover a large hole in the bottom or side of a boat, you will not have the old planking as a pattern. The procedure is to cut back from the edges of the hole and to cut scarphs in the surrounding planks. Measure the width of the hole and divide that by the number of planks required, including the width of the lands. The next stage is to use a spile board, which will provide a pattern for each plank.

Any knots should be cut away and faced with graving pieces cold-glued in. Broken timbers should be doubled up.

The hooked scarph is only used on such large pieces of timber as keels, where there is considerable longitudinal pull. In lighter construction it is common to use tablings – blocks of wood, the width of the timber, let into the face of the scarph. Rectangular dowels can also be used in the face of the scarph, as these add somewhat to the strength of the joint and stop the scarph from slipping about when the cramps are put on. Scarphs in the gunwale or stringer are cut the

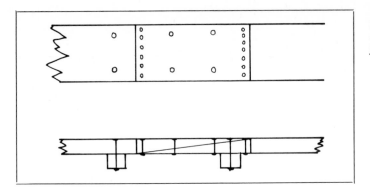

Repairs to clinker planking: Butt joints are quite unsuitable. All new planks will have to be scarph-jointed to old ones

opposite way to those in the keel, because they can be fitted and glued up in the boat, a stiffish bit of timber being placed outside the boat to take up the marks of the cramps and to keep the boat fair until the glue sets.

Spiling. This is the method of using a divider or compass to transfer the curve or shape from the existing plank to either a spile board or template or to the new plank. The spile board or new plank is offered up inside the boat as near as possible to the curve; the compass is then opened up and kept at the horizontal and moved along the curve making a line or a series of marks on the spile board or the new plank. This line or series of marks should give the required curve, but one should saw outside the line so that any unfairness can be adjusted when it is offered up.

With a piece of chalk, mark the width of the plank required. Do this at 2ft intervals along the length of the hole to be filled. Now, with a length of 3in × $\frac{1}{4}$in board, take a spile of the bottom plank. The spile board must be lying flush against the timbers and clamped to them. A line parallel to the top edge of the last undamaged plank is marked on the spile board with a pair of compasses. The width of the plank is also marked on the spile board from the chalk marks previously made. Finally, the position of the scarphs are marked in. The spile board is placed on top of the board from which the new plank is to be cut. Adjust its position on the board to make use of the most knot-free timber, then, with either a wire bit or a small morse drill, bore through the spile board at 1ft intervals on the line made with the compasses. Also bore through the line of the scarph. Mark the width from the chalk marks and then remove the spile board. A line of drilled holes will now be visible on the board. Spring a 1in × $\frac{3}{4}$in batten along the line of these holes and tack it down. Draw a line along the batten, then shift the batten up to the width marks and draw the line of the top of the plank. The plank can now be sawn out and planed up. When this has been done, offer it up and check the scarph marks for accuracy. Then, with a short straightedge, which should be precisely the width of the plank, see how much brow, if any, is required. Now cut and plane the scarph, plane the brow and fit and fasten the plank, including of course gluing the scarphs.

Carvel Planking Carvel planking does not suffer from land damage, as it has no overlap, nor does it tend to split along the fastenings. Planking may, however, be infected with rot from time to time. Should this happen, make a careful survey. If the rot lies in only a small area, first remove the paint from the infected planks for a distance of at least 4ft all round. You will then see the fastenings, which of course run through the timbers. Cut out the infected planking to an area well clear of the damaged wood. The new joints in carvel planking need not be scarph joints, but can be butt joints, which are cut square through the full thickness of the plank. Cut this joint midway between two timbers. Drill a hole and cut the plank with a keyhole saw. Remove the plank by cutting through the nails with a chisel held at an angle of 45° and driven into the plank about ¾in from the nail. Use an old chisel for this. Some force will be needed to remove the plank, and it will probably be necessary to get inside the boat and drive it off with a large hammer.

Having got the plank out, remove the nails and then clean up the butts at each end. Mark out a new plank, using the old one as a pattern, bevel the edges of the plank to suit the old one, and do not forget the caulking bevel, which should be about one-third of the width of the plank thickness. Fit a butt strap behind each butt, wide enough to overlap about ¾in on the planks above and below the new plank and long enough to fit snugly between the timbers or frames. Fasten the butt strap with copper nails and rooves in every plank that it touches, and also glue behind it.

Diagonal Planking   This is by far the most difficult kind of planking to repair. The nature of the construction makes it necessary to remove a great many outside planks to get at just one inside plank, and the number of fastenings used make it difficult to remove the planks.

If there is only a small hole through the planking, made, for instance, by an anchor fluke, it may be possible to effect a repair by removing a small piece of plank on the outside just bigger than the hole and gluing a graving piece firmly into place. The inner skin will have to be dealt with from inside the boat. Push the ragged pieces of wood back into the hole, cutting off any that cannot be returned, and fit a thin wooden patch, with the edges well chamfered, and screw down tightly, using plenty of bedding (white lead) beneath it.

If it is necessary to do a major repair, the planking will almost surely have to be destroyed in order to remove it. Before starting the removal, measure the width of the planking at various places and make notes. This will help later on when fitting the new planks. When sufficient planking has been removed, you may repair the inner skin as necessary. Fit a piece of calico or thin sailcloth in the hole and tack it down to the inner skin. Then, as the outer skin is replaced, lay a coat of white lead mixed with grease under the planking.

Double Planking   In large craft, such as sailing barges, it is most difficult to replace the inside planking. The mixture of cow hair and tar, or the modern equivalent of tarred felt, between the skins of a barge preserves the outer skin but not the inner one, where rot may often be present. The best one can do is to soak the inner skin with fungicide and put an extra layer of planking on the outside.

Sheathing an Old Hull with GRP   This work should not be undertaken until the hull has thoroughly dried out. Seams should be raked out and then filled with resin putty. Any scrapes or gashes should also be filled with resin putty or with graving pieces. Any oil contamination should be removed with carbon tetrachloride. The hull should then be sanded down, by means of a portable disc sander and coarse grit, to provide a key for the polyester resin. All ironwork, keelbands, etc, should be removed. A sufficient area of hull should be coated with resin

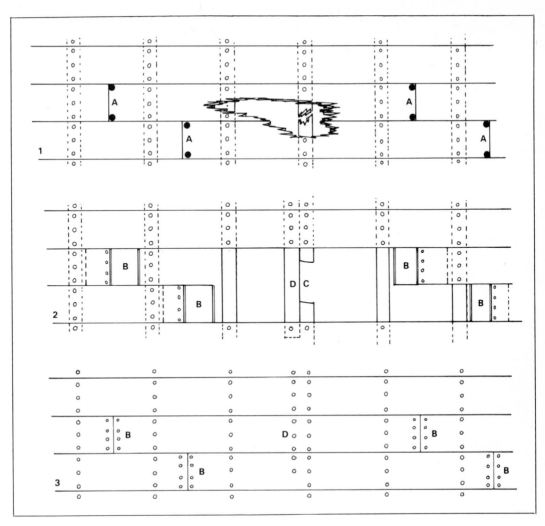

to take the first piece of glass cloth, which should then be given another liberal coating of resin.

For clinker or lapstrake planking, work from the deckline downwards, because of the lands. In fact, with this type of construction, it is best to do it plank by plank, covering one plank completely, then moving down to the next one below, each time overlapping the edges of the cloth. At both stempost and sternpost overlap the glass mat. It is advisable to put on three layers of sheathing.

For carvel or diagonal planking, one should start from the bottom of the keel and work upwards and outwards.

If such sheathing is done carefully, it should make a hull absolutely watertight; it will also strengthen the hull and provide protection against teredo or gribble. When the sheathing has been completed, lightly sandpaper the surface (by hand) and apply the final coat of polyester resin in whatever colour you wish.

Repairs to carvel planking:
1 Hole extending over two planks with one broken timber
(A) Holes drilled for keyhole saw to cut out damaged planks
2 The two damaged planks are cut out so that butt joints at the ends of the two planks will not come between the same pair of frames
(B) Butt pads in position
(C) Damaged ends of broken timber cut back
(D) Sister frame in position and side-fastened to broken frame
3 Replacement planks in position and fastened
(B) Butt-pad fastening

Deck Repairs and Replacements

In old vessels that are of any size one of the first places where rot will set in is the deck. It usually occurs where the deck is cut for masts,

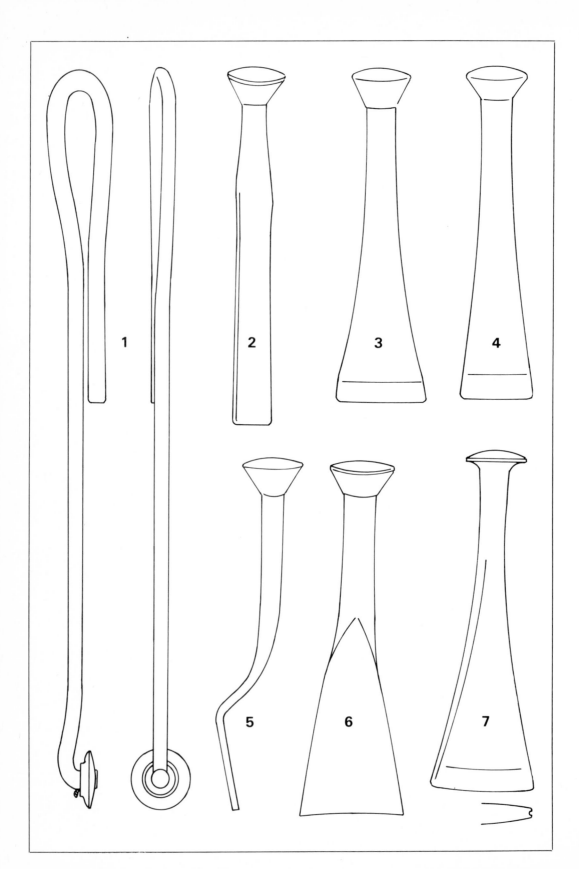

Caulking tools:
1 A caulking wheel is used for caulking thin planking ($\frac{5}{8}$in or $\frac{1}{2}$in). It is pulled towards the caulker, not pushed along the seam, thus driving the single strand of cotton home
2 A narrow-bladed iron called a spike is used for caulking awkward corners
3 The wedge iron has a thick blade and not much taper, and is designed for widening seams
4 The making iron has a square-ended blade of varying thickness. The cotton or oakum after being laid in the seam in loops is lightly drawn in by means of the making iron
5 and 6 For awkward seams such as garboards, a bent iron is used
7 After driving the cotton or oakum into the seams with the making iron, the caulker changes to a creasing iron, which has a hollow tip. With this tool he drives the caulking hard down into the seam and about $\frac{1}{8}$in below the surface of the planks. The caulking is now ready for paying

---

hatchways or cabin trunkings, and also in the covering boards where the bulwark stanchions are fitted.

Laid Decks If the deck beams and shelves (sheerclamps) are sound, redecking a vessel is not a great problem. In finely built old yachts laid decks either run fore and aft parallel with the centre line of the craft, or curve to follow the line of the hull, with the ends notched into the kingplank. Such curved planks are sprung into position. Larch or teak planks, 2in × 2in, can be used in vessels between 30ft and 50ft long. Planks of this thickness can be secret-fastened (blind-nailed) or screwed or spiked down, the heads of the screws being countersunk and plugged.

In relaying straight-planked decks work from the kingplank outwards; if the planks are curved, work from the covering board inwards. The ends of the planks that notch into the kingplank or into the covering board need to be varnished (for bright decks) or painted. For secret-fastening use galvanised nails, driving one or two into each deck beam.

Wood swells when wet and shrinks when dry, and hardwoods shrink and swell more than softwoods. So, in repairing the planking or the timbers of a boat, make allowance for these factors. This shrinking or swelling is most evident in the direction of the annular rings, and all planking should be fastened with the annular rings curved downwards or inwards. The same thing applies to beams and timbers. The swelling of the timbers when they are wet helps the boat to take up and give you a watertight hull. It also causes jamming hatchways and floorboards that cannot be lifted. In all joinery and cabinet work, therefore, allowances must be made for this. With tongue and groove always use planks with a mitre joint; this will stop the tongue and groove from lifting and buckling up. When laying a tongue and groove deck with seasoned timber, do not drive the tongue right into the groove; doing that will not allow space for the planks to swell. With unseasoned timber (ie normal kiln-dried pine) drive the tongue right home; it will shrink before you have finished your work, but will take up once the boat is in the water.

Caulking Oakum was the traditional material for caulking wooden-ships in Great Britain, but cotton seems to have been preferred in the USA. Oakum certainly lasts longer. It was picked from old hemp ropes by convicts, and, before it could be used for caulking, had to be spun by rolling with the flat of the hand over a length of canvas resting on the caulker's knee. Today oakum is spun by machinery, but it still needs to be teased and rolled.

Caulking decks. Planked decks are always laid with the heart of the wood facing downwards. To receive the caulking a V-cut is made between the planks to about two-thirds of their thickness. With oakum use one thread for every inch of the plank's thickness, the thread being about the width of the open seam. The first thread is laid in straight and driven right home to the bottom of the cut. A 6in caulking iron with a blade $2\frac{1}{4}$in and an edge $\frac{1}{64}$in thick is used to drive it home. If you are caulking a very heavy deck, coil a second thread of oakum and drive it hard into the V-cut. Finally a third and last thread is closely coiled and driven home. The caulking mallets are made of boxwood or other very hard wood with 18in-long ash handles, and each face of the mallet is bound with an iron or copper ring. The oakum now has to be dressed by means of a crease iron, which has a thicker edge ($\frac{5}{32}$in thick) than the caulking iron, and the edge has a recessed V-groove.

A depth in the seam equal to the width of the seam is left to receive the hot pitch, which is poured from ladles. Pitch can be heated in galvanised buckets held over a Propane burner. The overflow is scraped off the planking when the pitch is cold. Most professional boatbuilders use either a marine glue or a special deck seam compound, such as Seamflex, but it is much more expensive than pitch. Tencofix Dik, which is used in Holland for the under-sealing of automobiles, is an effective alternative to pitch.

Caulking topsides and bottom planking. It is easy enough to pay the seams of a well laid deck, but it is a different matter paying the seams of bottom planking. On large ships a vegetable pitch was used for this work, and the seams were payed with a mop that was used with a thrusting and twisting action, so working the pitch into the seams. On yachts and small craft a round brush (still called a pitch mop) is used with a twisting motion to pay the seams. The marine glue or the caulking compound must not be too runny.

On some craft, such as Friendship sloops and Dutch fishing botters, the caulking is not payed in the deck seams. These seams were not pitched or puttied, the reason for not covering the cotton caulking being that it made it a much easier to caulk in extra lengths of cotton if the deck sprang a leak. If the bottom of a vessel is going to be copper-sheathed, the bottom seams are payed flush with the surface of the planking, but enough depth is left for spun yarn to be laid on top of the pitch before the copper sheathing is fitted.

Topside seams after caulking are filled with a flexible stopping and painted. A soft filling can be made up of beeswax, resin, linseed oil and turpentine. The proportions are $\frac{1}{4}$lb beeswax, $\frac{1}{2}$ pint linseed oil, $\frac{1}{4}$lb

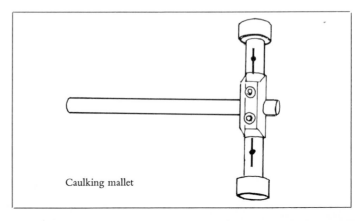

Caulking mallet

resin and 3oz turpentine. Grease mixed with ordinary putty makes a reasonably good flexible stopping.

Caulking with cotton. The cotton is sold in 1lb balls wound up from about 8 strands, each of about the thickness of ordinary double knitting wool. The seam is painted and the caulker begins by lightly driving the cotton in, in short loops or folds. The caulking iron has to be held horizontally and at right-angles to the seam; the hand is held facing upwards, so that if the mallet misses the caulking iron, it does not hit the knuckles. The loops should be just about driven home. After the cotton has been lightly driven into place for the full length of the seam, it is then driven hard home in the direction away from the stem. The object of the loops or folds is that when the ship is in the water and the planks start to swell, the looped cotton will bite into the sides of the seam rather than be ejected, as it probably would be if it was a smooth straight strand of cotton. It is easier to caulk softwood than hardwood, for which much firmer blows are needed.

In small, lightly planked craft candle wicking is used, and used without looping or folding. It is run into the seam by pulling a caulking wheel along the seam towards the caulker. This is a delicate operation. If the seam is too tight before caulking, it may be opened up slightly by running the caulking wheel along it.

After the cotton has been driven home, the seams are payed in the same manner as for oakum. For most small craft one of the proprietary compounds such as Seamflex are best used. They may be laid into the seams with a palette knife.

Canvas-covered Decks Decks and the tops of cabin trunks and hatches in old yachts were frequently covered with canvas. To re-canvas, first remove all the old canvas and fastenings. Clean down the surface with coarse-grained sandpaper and repair any damaged or soft spots, filling either with graving pieces or putty. Give the surface a coat of priming.

If the canvas is too narrow to cover the width of the deck or cabin top, sew two or more lengths together. This can be done on an ordinary sewing machine, using a heavy needle. A 10oz canvas is about right for weight.

Cut the canvas to fit, allowing plenty of spare to go over the edges, or up against the trunkings, so that quadrant battens can hold them in position. There is no need to canvas a kingplank that stands proud to the deck by $\frac{3}{4}$in or more; the deck canvas can be fitted to the edge of the kingplank. Tack the canvas down along the centre line and fold back on itself. It is a good idea to use a thin batten for the temporary fastening. The exposed side of the deck should now be thickly coated with sticky paint – any old paint in fact, including undercoating, but in this case mixed with varnish. The operative word is sticky.

When the paint is tacky, pull the canvas over it, wet it with a brush full of water and smooth it outwards from the centre until it fits snugly. Pin to the outside of the covering boards (or cabin sides) with copper tacks at 18in intervals, then cover the edge with a batten (half round, quadrant or flat), drill and fasten. Now remove the temporary centre line batten, fold back the canvas and repeat for the other side of the deck.

When the canvas is laid, give it a first priming coat, much diluted with linseed oil. To make the paint spread easily, work with two brushes, one loaded with water and the other with paint. Wet a patch about 18in square, paint it and continue in this fashion. The next coat is applied without water. The use of water for canvasing decks has long been practised in the Navy. The water helps the canvas both to stretch and not to absorb too much paint. It speeds up the painting very considerably. If you are using some form of glue, do not adopt this wetting method.

When joining two bits of canvas, say where the foredeck joins the side deck, overlap by 3in. Then turn the edge of the top piece under and tack it down with wide-headed copper tacks.

Jagged holes or places where the canvas has worn through should have the old canvas removed round the holes or worn places and cut to a neat square. Cut a new piece to overlap the edges of the hole by at least 2½in. The area below this should be coated with tacky paint, and a new piece of canvas, with edges turned in, should be stretched over it and tacked down with wide-headed copper tacks.

GRP-covered Decks GRP is much more durable than canvas and in many ways easier to handle. The deck should be prepared in the same manner as for canvasing, then coated with resin, on which the glass cloth should be laid down. Alternatively, the glass cloth can be laid down on the dry deck and a very liberal coating of resin applied to the top of it and allowed to soak through to the wood. As the resin soaks into the wood, it draws more resin through the glass cloth and seems to suck the mat down on to the deck. A second or third layer of resin can be put down if it is thought desirable. When it has completely hardened off, paint in the ordinary way.

In old boats with very uneven decks the best solution is to cover the deck with marine ply and coat that with GRP.

Marine Ply Covering for Decks It is essential to use best quality marine ply for any boat work (in Great Britain BS 1088). Even with this, care should be taken to seal all open ends, joints and flat surfaces. Special sealers are made for use on ply. To make sure of getting a clean sawcut, fasten a deal plank underneath and then saw through both ply and the deal. This will produce a clean edge.

The sealers should prevent crazing, ie a pattern of fine cracks that will show as soon as the surface is painted. These fine cracks, if not treated, can lead to delamination.

If you are laying a plywood deck on top of an old deck, bed down the sheets of ply on tarred felt (one proprietary brand of felt is called Fearnought). All joints should be scarphed and Cascophen-glued. Screws or nails should not be countersunk, but just driven in flush. *Never* drive nails or screws into the edges of single sheets of plywood. After a final coat of sealer, the deck can be painted with non-slip deck paint or coated with GRP.

A cheap alternative to marine ply is a waterproof hardboard, used smooth side downward, so that the patterned surface will give some grip on wet decks. It is difficult to cut a clean and true scarph in hardboard; therefore if you have any doubts about the closeness of the fit, do not glue but use some form of bedding-down compound.

Graving Pieces If a small area of the deck is damaged (perhaps as a result of dropping the point of an anchor fluke on it), it can be cut away with a keyhole saw. The cuts should be made vertically, and the traditional way to make the patch is diamond-shaped. A filling piece can be cut to fit and glued into position, and a butt pad fitted under the deck.

Covering Boards These outboard deck planks are usually thicker than the ordinary deck planks. If the deck planks are 1¾in thick, the covering board should be 2½in thick, and it is best to use a hardwood such as oak or locust, even if the deck planks are of larch or pine. With a moulded width of, say, 8in the covering board is made of a number of short lengths of plank. If the deck is made up of straight planks, the covering board may be notched to receive the ends of the planking. The short lengths of the covering board may be butted or hook-scarphed together. For scarphed joints, stopwaters should be used.

If the vessel has proper bulwarks, the covering board will be pierced for stanchions. A square hole is cut in the covering board for each square-sided stanchion, which is not caulked when fastened but sealed on each side with larch or cedar wedges, set down as hard as possible, then cut off flush with the top of the covering board.

In old vessels covering boards are almost the first things to show signs of rot, particularly where the stanchions pierce them. The simplest way of fastening stanchions is to screw them to the topside planking, and where possible to side-fasten to the frames.

If the covering boards have decayed badly, the ends of the deck beams may also have rotted. If they have rotted badly, the old beams will have to come out, but if it is only at the ends and along the tops of the beams, new pieces can be scarphed in.

Gunwales, Bulwarks and Stanchions Various English, Continental and American open fishing boats are not fitted with covering boards, so that the joints between the timbers and planks are exposed to the weather; likewise the end grain of the timber is unprotected, so that damp may penetrate and rot set in. (Paint is only a partial protection.) If this has happened, it may be necessary to cut back the timbers, first dismantling the gunwale. If the rot has not penetrated too deeply, it can be treated with a fungicide with good penetration powers, such as Woodtreat. The surfaces should first be thoroughly cleaned and dried, and then covered with a thick layer (¼in) of Woodtreat. Any new timbers should have their end grains coated with emulsion. For scarphs or any timber that has to be glued, use an organic solvent type of preservative, such as Brunophen 2.

In larger decked craft bulwarks are liable to both rot and damage. Treatment for this has already been covered (see p 13). If one can afford to use teak not only for the rail but also for the stanchions and covering boards, the future life of this vulnerable part of the ship could be almost unlimited.

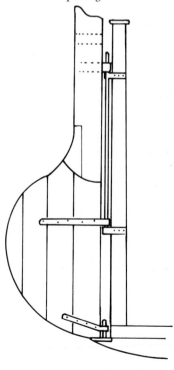

Construction of an outboard rudder, hung on a vertical rod and one pintle at the foot. The middle gudgeon is in the form of a split ring

Rudders

Rudders that may hang outboard on transom or Scandinavian sterns have heavy wooden stocks. Inboard rudders on boats with counters have either wooden or metal stocks. The outboard rudder for, say, a 5–7ton yacht or work boat should be made up from planks at least 1in thick. The average rudder for a boat of this size would be made up of three 9in planks joined by drift bolts. The plank nearest to the sternpost is carried up to the level of the tiller slot, or to the top of the stock if the vessel has wheel steering.

The blade and stock are cut to the shape of the old rudder and the gudgeons are fitted. These will have been cast or made up by a blacksmith or engineering works (see p 82), and can be fastened with riveted nails or through-bolts, depending on their size. The gudgeons act both as supports for the rudder and as strops to hold the blade together.

The cheekpieces (1in or 1¼in thick) are next fitted, nailed and riveted.

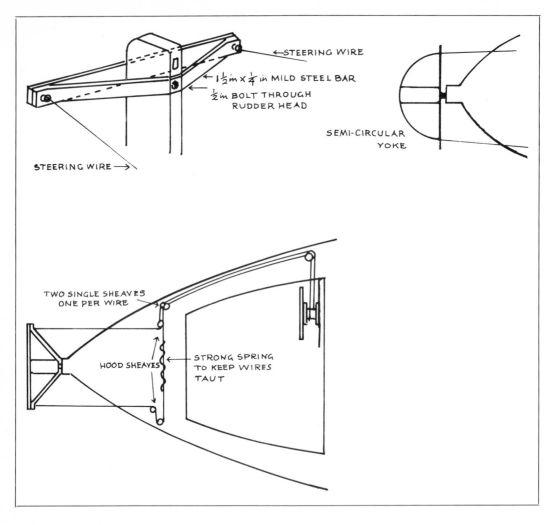

STEERING WIRE

1½ in × ¼ in MILD STEEL BAR

½ in BOLT THROUGH RUDDER HEAD

STEERING WIRE →

SEMI-CIRCULAR YOKE

TWO SINGLE SHEAVES ONE PER WIRE

HOOD SHEAVES

STRONG SPRING TO KEEP WIRES TAUT

Outboard rudders: details of a simple yoke for wheel-steering boats with pointed or transom sterns

If the rudder is to be steered with a tiller, a filling piece will be fitted between these cheeks above the tiller slot.

Some craft, such as lifeboats, have a steel rod running down the sternpost that acts as a pintle. The rudder hangs from this rod by one split gudgeon and one ring gudgeon that slips over the top of the rod.

Rudder stocks that pass through the counter should be made of bronze rod whenever possible, and fitted into a bronze tube with a diameter some ¼ in more than the rod. This is to replace the almost certainly rotten wooden stock and trunking. The head of the stock is squared to take a tiller or a quadrant for wheel steering. The wooden rudder blade is edge-fastened to the metal stock by bolts. The forward edge of the blade is cut to a concave section so that the stock fits snugly, and the after side of the sternpost should be similarly shaped.

The rudder tube should be just proud of the deck and be fitted with a flange. Likewise it should project just through the bottom of the counter. If this tube is to replace a wooden rudder trunk, no doubt new horn timbers and probably a new sternpost will have been fitted. In that case you will have to drill up through the counter and the horn timber, which is the centre supporting timber in the bottom of the counter. To make sure the rudder tube is a very tight fit, drill the hole to give a driving fit, and thread the bottom few inches of the tube, so that

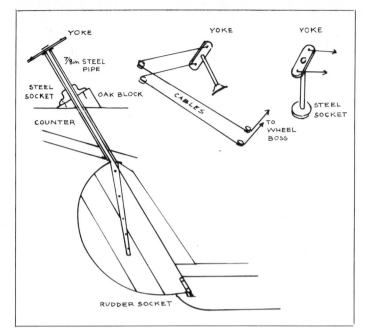

Inboard rudders: details of yoke and rudder

it can get a tight hold on the horn timber. Some care must be taken with alignment. The final job is to fit the pintles, which, with the gudgeons, the rudder tube and stock should all be of the same metal – preferably bronze.

The rudder trunking of craft with heavy wooden stocks may have to be rebuilt – an awkward job. The deck will certainly have to be taken off the counter. The trunking may have to be remade in a circular shape from eight or more pieces of hard wood. These should be impregnated with fungicide before caulking, which has to be done from inside the trunk. In spite of all precautions, such wooden trunks are a most likely breeding ground for fungal decay.

8

Setting Up
for Rebuilding and Repairing
Flat-bottomed Boats

When rebuilding or repairing small boats, such as dories, gun punts or other 'flatties', you will find the work is made much easier if you set up a building horse. This is made up from a plank on edge – about 2in thick, 9in high and at least as long as the centre line of the bottom of the boat – supported at either end with legs. In addition you need a pair of trestles 2ft 3in high and 3ft wide.

If it is a complete rebuild, the new flat bottom of the boat is made up on the trestles. If you are using planks (rather than marine ply), the centre plank will be cut longer than the ones on either side, to save timber. These planks can be tightly cramped together by means of a Spanish windlass or, if they are available, with sash cramps. The centre line of the boat is marked in by stretching a chalked line between two

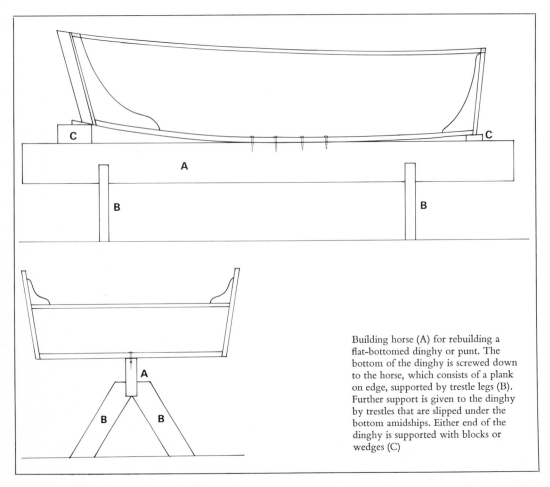

Building horse (A) for rebuilding a flat-bottomed dinghy or punt. The bottom of the dinghy is screwed down to the horse, which consists of a plank on edge, supported by trestle legs (B). Further support is given to the dinghy by trestles that are slipped under the bottom amidships. Either end of the dinghy is supported with blocks or wedges (C)

nails and then flicking it against the centre plank. The planks are then held together with temporary wooden straps. Stations are marked and the planks are cut to the shape of the bottom. The proper floor timbers are then made up, placed in position and holes for the fastenings drilled through timbers and planks. These are then fastened, the copper nails being driven up from underneath and the rooves clenched on the top of the timbers.

Stempost, sternpost and timbers to support the planking are made up and nailed into position, patterns for all of these being taken from the old boat. The boat is now lifted off the trestles and placed on the horse. Such fore and aft rise as there may be is taken care of by means of chocks fastened to the horse. The bottom of the boat is screwed down (on its centre line) to the horse and the trestles are slid underneath to provide a firm platform on which to work. The object of the horse is to ensure you get the correct fore and aft rise in the bottom of the boat.

The sides are then planked up and fastened to stempost and sternpost (or transom) and to the timbers or knees. Timbers can be made up from grown knees or cut from marine ply, or they can be straight lengths of timber joined to the floor timbers with galvanised frame clips. This is how dories are framed.

The stempost can be made up from a grown crook, with rebates cut in it for the forward end of the planks. It could be made up in two pieces from straight lengths of timber. The inner becomes the apron to which

Bow view of a naval cutter in frame, but planked up above wale strake. Painted by Joseph Marshall 1775 (*Science Museum*)

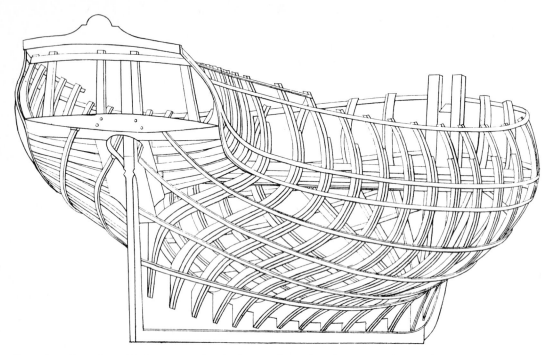

Stern view of a small vessel in frame
c1760 from William Falconer's
Dictionary of the Marine. Note fore and
aft ribands holding frames in position

Stempost cut from a grown crook for a
flat-bottomed dinghy, and overlapping
stem as in dory construction

the planking is fastened without any rebates. The stem now overlaps
both the apron and planking. It is through-bolted. Before being fastened,
the surfaces are liberally coated with lead paint, and a piece of canvas
soaked in linseed oil is slipped between them. When the stem is fastened,
the overlapping canvas is trimmed off with a razor blade.

This false stem is often a solution to badly damaged hoodends, ie
where the ends of the planks are screwed to the stem. The old stem and
the ends of the planking are sawn off flush. The planks are refastened
to a new apron and a new stempost overlaps both plank ends and apron.

Lofting   In building a new boat it is most desirable to lay off the lines
full size on a loft floor. This not only helps the boat builder to visualise

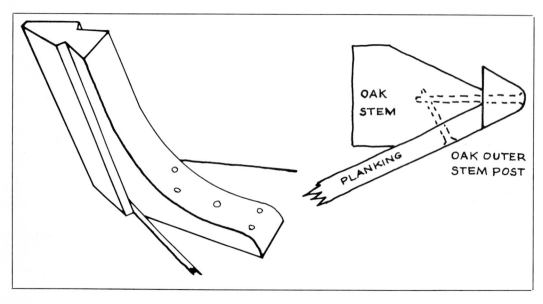

what the boat will look like when she is built, but also enables him to make up exact patterns of such things as the keel pieces, the stem and stern assemblies, etc, in light plywood, $\frac{1}{4}$in cedar or hardboard. These patterns can then be juggled about on uncut timber stock until all the pieces can be cut to the best advantage.

Ideally a proper mould loft is required, where the whole drawing can be left on the floor and referred to as required. It is most unlikely that anyone rebuilding an old boat would have access to a mould loft, but a passable loft floor can be made out of sheets of plywood framed by 2in × 1in battens. The time spent in making a good surface for lofting is not wasted, as the more thorough the lofting is, the easier it becomes to build the boat and the less likely are you to make expensive mistakes.

The drawing surface should be made as wide as the boat is deep, from the highest point to the lowest each side of the waterline, or half the beam, whichever is the greater plus an extra 2ft. On this surface the profile, ie the side view and half the breadth, can be laid out – one superimposed upon the other. The diagonals can also be drawn upon this surface. For the body plan it is a good idea to prepare a separate plywood surface. This keeps the size of the lofting surface to more manageable dimensions.

An essential tool both for measuring and scribing is a bevel gauge, which can be made up from two strips of brass joined together by a screw.

If you draw your lines in with chalk, leave the ply surface unpainted. On the other hand, a couple of coats of flat white paint will show up pencil or scribed lines much more clearly. An article by Jim Emmett in the now out of print *Classic Boat Monthly* of February 1973 gave some useful hints on laying down lines. From the designer's table of offsets the proper distances from a base line are marked in, the battens are bent along these marks to a fair curve and the resulting lines are then scribed. From the waterline and buttocks the points for the half-sections can be taken. You will need a pair of dividers and a very large setsquare, each about 8ft long. The latter can be made up from a sheet of 8ft × 4ft plywood. The dividers are most useful in the drawing out of stem and stern assemblies and the keel. Station lines are marked out on the backbone assembly.

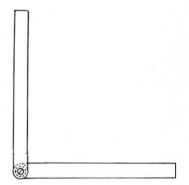

Bevel gauge. The blade should not be less than 9in long

9
Hatch and Coach-house Construction

There are as many ways of making hatches, and as many different kinds of hatch, as there are boatbuilders. For instance, lift-off hatches or hinged hatches should be mounted on the deck, so that the hatch coamings can be fastened up from underneath the deck; but whenever possible, position the coamings above the deck beams. In this case the coamings will be screwed down through the deck into the deck beams. The screw heads should be well countersunk and dowelled over.

Sliding hatch with wash boards tapered to avoid jamming, designed by Maurice Griffiths, GM

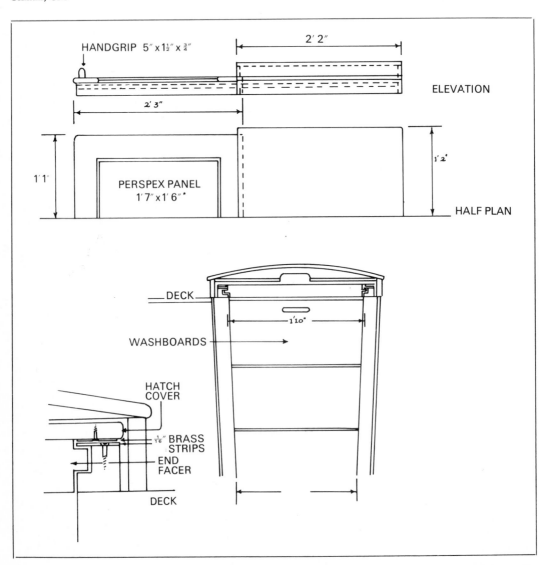

When making hatches of this type, make both the casing (the lid) and the coamings (the framework sitting on the deck) in one piece, then cut through horizontally with a circular saw. In this way they are bound to fit exactly. The coamings and the casings should be dovetail-jointed. After the coamings have been screwed into position, they are lined with hardwood, which will project upwards above the coamings by half an inch and at the bottom will cover the thickness of the deck. The corners are mitred and the lining should be well bedded down. The casing of the hatch will then fit over the hardwood, which acts as a rebate and helps to keep out some of the wet.

Sliding Hatches   A certain amount of care is needed in the planning of sliding hatches. They should be longer fore and aft than they are wide, and should be made of some durable material that will not move in extremes of weather. Aluminium alloys make good hatch covers, and, of the timbers, teak, iroko or Honduras mahogany are the best, probably in that order. No hard and fast rules apply to the construction of sliding hatches. If the hatches are to be made to the drawings of a competent

Waterproof lifting hatch, designed by Maurice Griffiths, GM

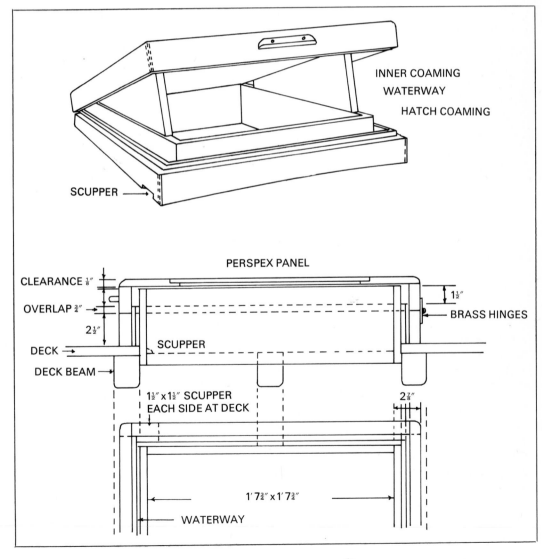

Fitting a new wheelhouse and decking to an open Scandinavian boat. (1) Foredeck and bulkhead are framed and foredeck beam of wheelhouse has been fitted. (2) Deck beams and carlines are in position, and the front of the deckhouse is being offered up. (3) Wheelhouse is in position. The sides and top are of marine ply. (4) The conversion is complete (*Richard Riggs*)

designer, all the shipwright has to do is to follow the drawings. In restoration work, and where no drawings exist, it is best to make the hatch runners with a groove on the outside to prevent the hatch lifting off.

Since the main object of a sliding hatch is to slide, it is essential that the top edges of the runners are straight and without any twist or 'wind'. This can be checked by means of two small straight-edges placed one at each end transversely across the runners. It is then possible to see if there is any error. It is equally important to make sure that the hatch cover is square and that the runners are absolutely flat.

Large heavy hatches need to have the running surfaces sheathed with brass or tufnel. The latter material, which is also used for stern-tube bearings, is very good for this job. Use $\frac{3}{16}$in brass or tufnel cut as wide

as the runners are thick. Fasten down very securely with accurately driven and countersunk screws. Brass runners always need greasing.

Leak-proof Hatches The only method of building leak-proof hatches that I know of was devised many years ago by Maurice Griffiths. It is complicated to build, because the hatch has double coamings, but the designer's drawings show the construction very clearly (see diagram).

Cabin Trunks Cabin trunks (or coach-house roofs) are constructed on the same principle as hatchways. There are basically two ways of making up trunks: one is to fix the carlines below the decks and screw the sides of the cabin trunk to them; and the other is to have double carlines, above and below the deck, with the cabin sides seated on the

Opening wheelhouse window. The design is based on the old-fashioned railway carriage principle

Simple plywood frame to support cabin trunk

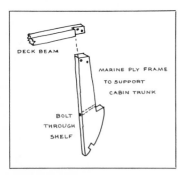

Framing a new wheelhouse by an amateur shipwright. The boat is the motor cruiser *Reva* lying at West Mersea (*Keith Mirams*)

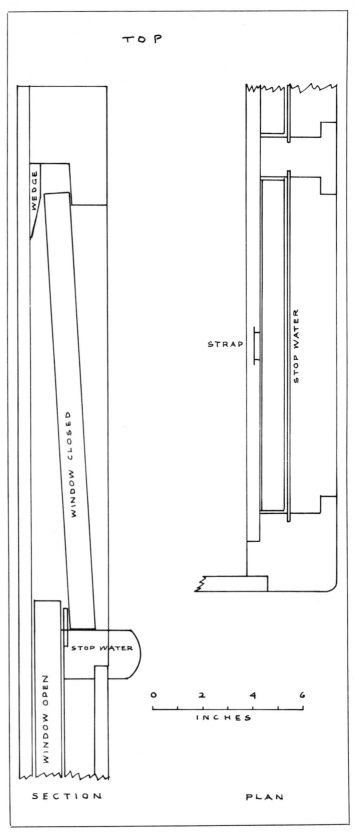

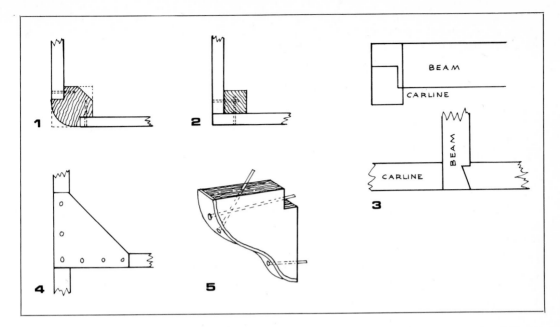

deck *outside* the carlines, to which they are screwed. I have had a cabin trunk like this for 15 years and it has never let in a drop of water.

The most satisfactory way of joining the sides and the fronts or backs is by rebating them into a corner post. A less expensive method is to butt them up to each other, with a triangular post inside to which they are fastened.

Carlines for the roof beams are fitted along the insides of the trunk sides. Slots are cut in these and the roof beams are half-slotted into them. The tops of the beams are bevelled to allow for the fore and aft slope. The top can then be tongue-and-groove planked or covered with marine ply.

Wheelhouse Windows The diagram here shows a window that opens on the old-fashioned railway carriage principle. A strap could be fitted to the bottom of the frame, but we have not found this necessary in our wheelhouse. When closing the window, lift it up by the top of the frame over the brass strip that acts as a stopwater, and drop it down on to the sill outside the stopwater. Such windows are effective and tolerably waterproof. They can be glazed with plate glass or perspex.

Rabbets (or Rebates) Rabbets are used when joining one piece of wood to another and leaving them flush on one side – for example, the corner posts of cabin trunks. Rabbets are usually cut by means of the circular saw, with the blade wound down to the depth of the rebate. They can be cut by hand saw and finished with a rabbet plane. Where the level of the rabbet is altering all the time, as on a stempost, it can only be cut with a mallet and chisel or an adze. In such cases considerable care is necessary to arrive at a satisfactory result.

1 Rabbeted corner post for cabin trunk, cut from a piece of 4in × 4in hardwood
2 Butt-jointed corner for cabin trunk with corner post
3 Dovetail joint for joining deck beams to carlines
4 Triangular web of marine ply screwed to beam and shelf or carline acting as a lodging knee
5 Hanging knee made up from three layers of marine ply glued together and faced with Canadian rock elm

10

Spars,
Cleats and Tabernacles

At one time nearly all yacht masts, whether solid or hollow, were made of spruce. The best spruce came from Sitka, the one-time capital of Alaska. In heavier vessels pitch pine was used, as well as British Columbian pine and Oregon pine. Cheaper boats used Norway fir. The ideal was to get a tree as near as you could to the size of the finished mast. The bark was trimmed, and as little wood as possible was planed off to make the stick fair and straight. It was then varnished.

Solid masts and spars are best made from tree trunks rather than sawn timber, which is often cut so that the stick is cross-grained, or with the heart exposed down one side of the stick. If a spar has to be sawn, make sure the heart wood is in the centre of the spar, or have it cut out so that there is none in the spar at all. The annular rings should run transversely across the spar, and not fore and aft. A sawn stick, with the heart wood down the middle, may well have a bend. If this cannot be corrected when shaping up the stick, arrange it so that the mast bends aft; the bend can then be corrected by the pull of the forestay.

If the spar is sawn square, shape it as follows. Stick a bradawl in each end on the centre line and stretch a chalk line tightly from end to end and about $\frac{1}{4}$in above the surface. Now, with your eye immediately above the chalk line, make a series of pencil marks at 4in intervals directly below the line. Remove the line, and with as long a straight-edge as possible connect up the pencil marks. When this line has been ruled in, look along it to make sure that it is quite straight. From this centre line mark the width of the spar at various points, taking these measurements from the spar drawing. Connect up these marks with a straightedge. The shape of the spar will now be drawn out on one face of this square-sectioned timber. Remove the wood outside the lines from the two adjoining faces by saw and plane, or with an adze, being very careful to keep the timber square at all times. Having removed the unwanted wood, look along the spar to see that it is quite fair. Then turn the spar on its side and do the same thing over again. This will leave you with a square-sectioned spar correctly tapered. The next stage is to convert this four-sided spar into an eight-sided spar, which is simpler than it sounds, for all one needs is an eight-square gauge and that is quite easy to make.

With the gauge mark the spar on all four sides and remove the surplus wood. This can be done with an adze or a draw knife and plane. Having planed it down the gauge lines, round it off with a draw knife and finish off with a plane, scraper and sandpaper. The sandpaper should be used with a spiral motion. When the spar is almost finished, run your hand along it, as small bumps and unevennesses that cannot be seen can usually be felt.

For large spars made up from tree trunks, scribe circles to give the exact size of the finished spar at top and foot. If the stick is out of the true, these circles may not have their centres in the middle of the tree,

A spar gauge is made up on the 5:12 principle, ie the distance between the copper-covered wedge points is 12in and that between the scribing points is 5in. When using the gauge, make sure the points touch both sides of the spar. This gauge is suitable for spars from 4in to 12in in diameter. For thicker spars a larger gauge to the same proportions would have to be made up. Nos 1 and 2 are the copper-covered points and 3 and 4 are the scribing points

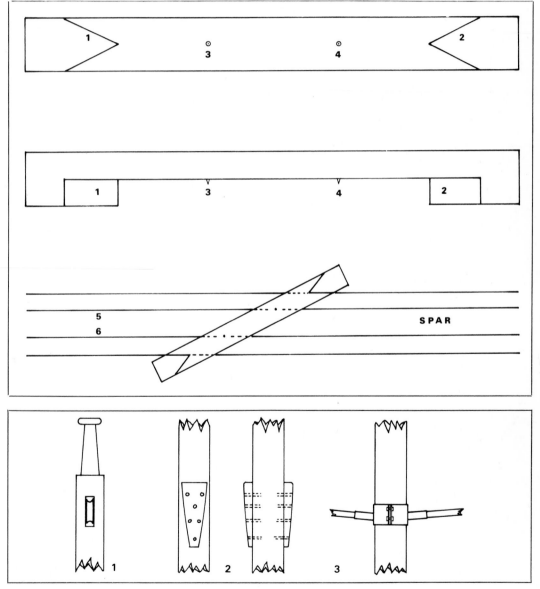

Mast construction:
1 Head of mast, showing truck, pole, shoulders and sheave
2 The bolsters at the hounds, side and front views

Construction of a hollow spar:
1 Section of a completed spar
2 Half the spar hollowed on the inside; the small hollow is for the luff rope
3 Mould for outside of spar
4 Feather-edge scarphs on each side of mast. These must be as far apart from each other as possible
5 Section of a square box spar with sail track

so draw horizontal and vertical lines through them, marking the points where they touch the outside of the stick. Stretch chalked lines along the length of the timber. Clear the unwanted timber until you have come near to the circumference of the circle, then follow the practice outlined above.

The fitting of bolsters below the hounds, and of spreaders or cross-trees, is done as shown in the drawing. Spreaders should be firmly fastened to the mast and held together by bronze or galvanised steel straps.

Hollow Spars   The making of hollow spars is not a job to be under-taken lightly. It is a craft that needs not only great accuracy in cutting

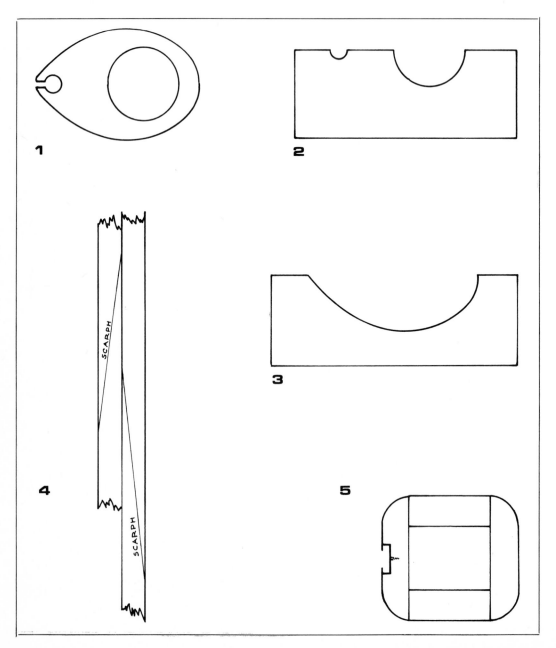

and fitting scarphs, but also considerable dexterity and speed in gluing, and a certain amount of special equipment, including a long flat surface (as long as the mast) and a number of cramps of different sizes. There are, however, certain kinds of spar that are relatively simple to make. These are either square-sectioned box spars or oval-sectioned hollow spars. In both cases the halliards can be made to run down the centre of the mast, and with oval-sectioned spars an additional track for the luff rope of the mainsail can be built into the after edge of the spar.

Square-sectioned masts are nothing more than elongated wooden boxes. The four sides are glued and screwed together, with packing pieces at 4ft intervals and at the points from which the shrouds and stays lead. The square corners are rounded off after gluing, and a track for the mainsail is fitted on the after side.

In the oval-sectioned mast the after edge is straight, for all the tapering is done on the fore and aft line on the fore side. With such scarphs as are necessary, make up a long enough piece of timber for each half of the spar. Cramp these halves together and plane off the taper on the fore side. Uncramp the two halves and lay them on the bench.

When scarphing a spar, choose a feather-edge scarph, which is best. This scarph should be about eight times the thickness of the timber in length. Having marked the scarph on both pieces of timber, cut them as nearly as possible to size, then place them on the bench, turn the shortest of the two pieces end for end and cramp it on top of the other piece, so that the two cut scarphs form one long flat surface. Now finish both surfaces off with a trying plane, and a perfect fit should result.

Damaged Spars If a spar is damaged or has a soft patch in it, the broken or rotten area should be cut out, the spar treated with fungicide and a new piece scarphed in. If it is just a small area, a graving piece can be let in, as on a deck plank, then planed to the shape of the mast.

If a solid spar is broken, say two-thirds from the top, reshape the bottom piece as in the diagram, and cut the new length of spar to fit over this male member. The surfaces should fay exactly, then be Cascophen-glued and clamped together.

Repairs to broken and damaged spars:
1 Wedge-shaped scarph for joining new piece to a broken spar
2 Repairs to a soft patch in a spar

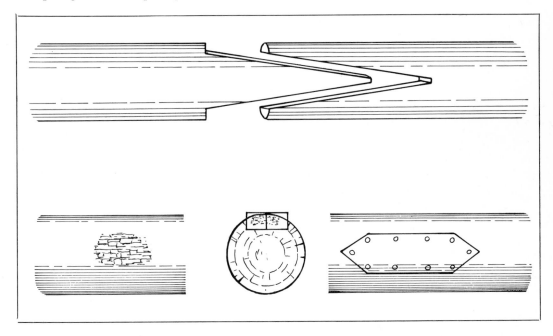

Cleats:
1 Common cleat
2 Thumb cleat
3 Roller cleat
4 Comb cleat
5 Sheet cleat
6 Shroud cleat
7 Halliard cleat

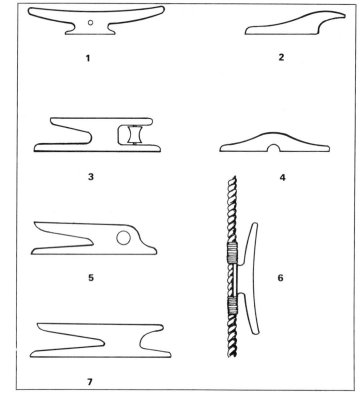

Bollards:
1 Cast mild-steel bollard through-bolted to hardwood pad below deck
2 and 3 Staghorn, three-quarter and side view, cut from a grown oak crook and side-bolted below deck to a frame. Alternatively it can be supported by a knee fastened through the deck to a hardwood pad

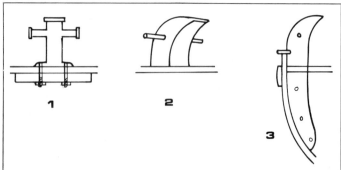

Cleats, Bollards and Staghorns Cleats are of different sizes and different shapes, depending on the size and purpose of the ropes made fast to them. There are seven basic types. They need to be made of straight grained hardwood, usually mahogany, though oak or elm can be used. They can be bought from yacht chandlers, but it is more satisfying to make them.

Bollards and staghorns can be made of timber or metal. Staghorns, which are commonly found in traditional Dutch boats, are like knight-heads, curved inboard and pierced fore and aft either with a metal or hardwood pin to prevent the lines from slipping over the top. They can either pierce the deck (as in diagram) like stanchions and be bolted to the topsides and where possible side fastened to the nearest frame. Or they can rest on the deck and be held by an inverted knee that is through-bolted to a pad below the deck.

When all that work seems worthwhile:
Hyacinth, Colchester smack built in
1901 and professionally restored for
Mrs Mollie Kennell in the 1970s
(*Keith Mirams*)

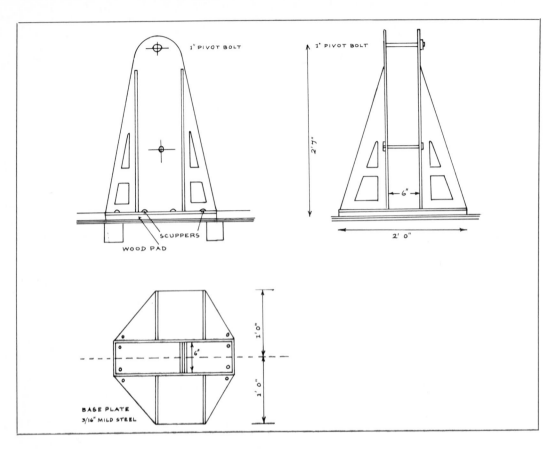

Galvanised steel tabernacle (from
drawings by J. Francis Jones)

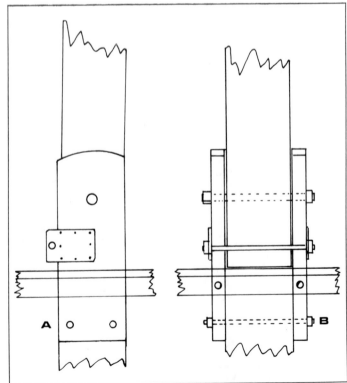

Side and front views of a wooden
tabernacle used in Dutch craft

Tabernacles These need to be made up from mild steel plate and bolted through the deck to a hardwood pad. The thrust of the mast will have to be taken by one or two supports of galvanised iron tube going down to the mast step, fastened across the hog or kelson or bridging two floors.

The tabernacle in the diagram was designed by J. Francis Jones for an 8-ton sloop. It was welded in $\frac{3}{16}$in mild steel plate and measures 2ft 7in from deck to pivot bolt. For smaller craft this height can be reduced by at least 9in.

For traditional craft, such as Dutch fishing boats, the tabernacle is made up from a heavy, square timber post, which rests on a mast step to which two 2in × 7in timbers are bolted. The mast pivots on a 1in bolt, 5in from the top of the tabernacle. When the mast is raised on either of these tabernacles, it is clamped in position by another bolt, fixed in the case of the wooden tabernacle, to plates on either side of the tabernacle and about 3in clear of the deck.

This wooden tabernacle can be supported by heavy knees on either side. Alternatively, the side supports can be taken down through the deck, as in the diagram, and bolted to the mast support.

I I

Metal Work

Mast, spar and rudder fittings for Bermudan-rigged boats can be bought
from yacht chandlers. For older types of boats they usually have to be
specially made up either from iron or bronze bars, forged and welded,
or they can be cast. Such casting is something that should only be done
in a proper foundry, for one is dealing with very high temperatures.
The lowest temperature at which even aluminium alloy will melt is
660°C. How such casting is done is of interest to anyone restoring or
repairing an old boat, for patterns in wood will have to be made up
for the foundry.

In the moulding of such small items as rowlocks or fairleads, two
bottomless boxes called the cope and the drag, which fit precisely
together, make up the moulding flask. These are filled with green sand
(a special foundry sand), which is damp and mixed with a certain
amount of clay and sometimes with molasses. The mixture has to be
permeable to allow for the escape of steam and gases when the hot
metal is poured into the mould, yet firm and sticky enough to remain
in the two halves of the flask when they are separated or turned upside
down. The impression, ie the matrix of the object to be cast, is made
from a wooden pattern, which must be slightly oversize to allow for
shrinkage and also for machining of the rough casting.

The process starts with the cope (the top half of the moulding flask)
being turned upside down and placed on a flat surface – the moulding
board. The cope is filled with sand, which is rammed down hard, then
'strickled off', flush with the surface of the box. A depression approximately the shape of the pattern is dug out of the surface with a spoon.
The pattern is dusted with talcum powder or fine sieved ash and is
placed in the depression, so that it is sunk to half its depth.

The drag is now placed on top of the cope and locked into position.
It is filled with sand, which is rammed down hard on to the top surface
of the cope and so of the pattern.

The two halves of the moulding flask, locked firmly together, are
turned over so that the cope is uppermost. The cope is then lifted off
revealing the drag with a precise impression of the pattern, and the
sand packed hard up against it. The sand is knocked out of the cope,
which is then replaced on the drag and refilled with sand. The two
sprue pins are put into position before the sand is completely filled in
and rammed down. The two pins are used respectively as a channel for
the molten metal and for allowing the surplus metal to rise up on the
other side of the mould. The sand is ventilated to allow moisture and
gases to escape, by poking a piece of wire down through it near the
pattern but not on it.

The sprue pins are withdrawn and the moulding flask once again
turned upside down. The pattern is loosened by tapping with the
rapping tool, then lifted out. There will now be precise impressions of
the pattern in each half of the moulding flask, and, in the cope, the two

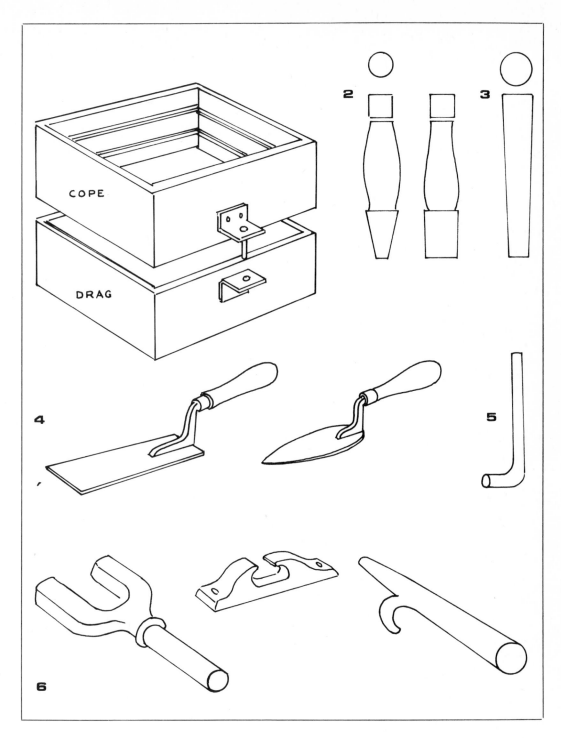

Moulding small units:

1 The cope and drag, which together make up the moulding flask, have horizontal ribs on their inner walls to assist in the retention of sand. There are brass plates on either side with interlocking pins

2 Wooden peg rammer, side and front views. It is 6½in high and used for firming the sand round the mould

3 Sprue pins, 5½in high, used for forming pouring and riser holes in the sand

4 Squared trowel and heart-shaped trowel for smoothing sand on surfaces of cope and drag, and for cutting ingates and channels along which the metal can flow

5 Rapping tool, 7in long, for tapping pattern to loosen it from the mould before drawing it out

6 Wooden patterns of rowlock, a fairlead and the head of a boathook, carved from softwood

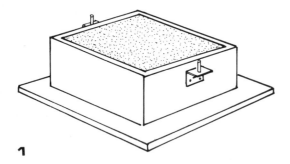

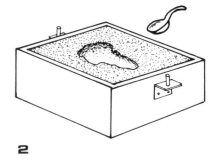

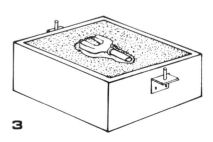

The moulding process:

1 The cope is inverted on the moulding board, filled with sand, which is rammed down hard and strickled off level with the top of the box

2 A shallow cavity approximately the size of the pattern is spooned out of the sand

3 The pattern of the rowlock is placed in the shallow cavity and dusted with talc or other parting powder

4 The drag is placed over the cope, filled with sand which is rammed down hard

5 The two boxes, locked together, are turned over so that the cope is uppermost

6 The cope is lifted off, showing the top of the sand in the drag with an impression of the pattern, with the sand packed tight round it

7 The sand is knocked out of the cope, which is replaced on top of the drag with sprue pins in position, filled with sand and rammed down hard. Wires are thrust into the sand to provide ventilation holes for gas and steam to escape

8 The sprue pins are withdrawn, flask inverted and the cope lifted off. Ingates and channels are cut. The pattern is removed, the cope is replaced and locked into position

9 Molten metal can now be poured into one of the holes made by the sprue pins

10 Section of the moulding flask

11 When the sand is removed, the casting will look like this. The castings formed from the pouring and riser holes are sawn off. The rowlock is now ready for final machining and polishing

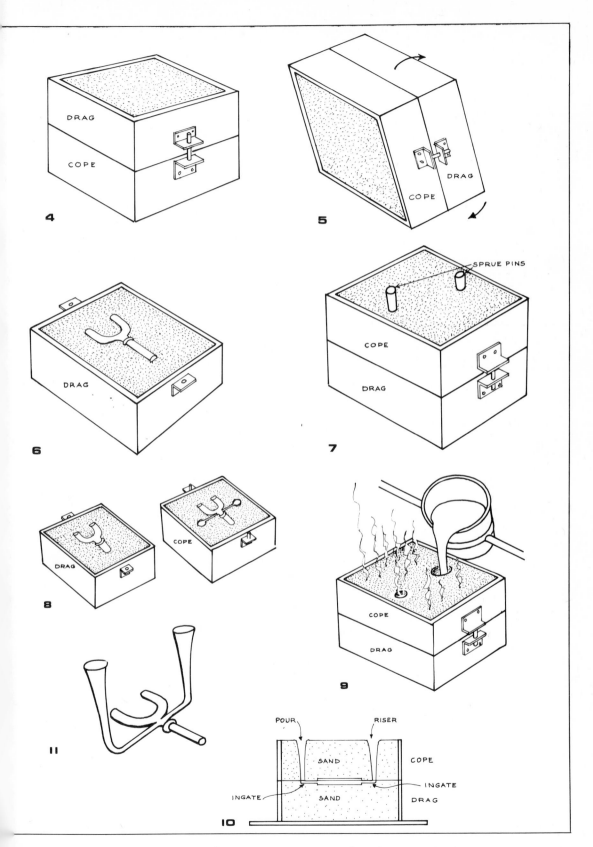

4

5

6

7

8

9

11

10

Iris, Colchester oyster dredger built at Brightlingsea in 1903 and restored by Charles Harker in the 1960s

holes made by the sprue pins. Channels (ingates) are cut from the sprue holes to the impression, so that when the molten metal is poured, it may run from the sprue hole right through the matrix, and finally, when that is filled, through the channel and up the riser.

After allowing time for cooling, the cope is lifted off, the sand breaking away from the cast object. The ingates are sawn off and the moulding is machined. The example illustrated here is a rowlock. In fact rowlocks could well be cast in pairs and then severed in the middle of the shank. With intricate castings, the difficulty is to ensure a good flow of metal into every part of the cavity.

Patterns These should be made up from any easily workable timber (even balsa wood would do), provided all the surfaces are sanded smooth and any declivities or cracks filled in with plastic wood. Allowances should be made in the pattern for ease of extraction from the mould. If, for instance, you were casting a pintle for a rudder, you should give the pin some taper. Allowances should be made for shrinkage; the amount should be checked with the foundry, for it varies with different metals

and alloys. When the pattern is completed, it should be given several coats of shellac. For commercial production, when the pattern is to be used several times, it is painted with a special paint that is resistant to attack from the CO_2 gas given off by the moulding sand. For a pattern, say of a keel, which is only to be used once, three coats of shellac would be quite adequate.

Casting a Lead Keel Lead is the one metal that can be safely cast away from a foundry. There are two ways of making the mould. One is by means of a pattern and casting sand in a large trough-like box; the other is to make up a mould box to the exact size of the ballast keel. Such a mould can be made up from $\frac{3}{4}$in or 1in deal planks. If there is any fore and aft taper, the side planks can be bent to shape around the bottom plank, which can be sawn to shape and if necessary given bevelled edges to supply an adequate flare. If there is any rocker to the keel, the bottom of the mould will have to be bent upwards and held in position by cross beams. The shape of the top of the mould can be maintained by transverse ribs.

Boadicea, Maldon oyster dredger built in 1808 and rebuilt by Michael Frost in the 1960s

87

The mould should be sunk in a piece of level ground, with the earth tamped down firmly round it. If you have to heat the lead indoors place the mould under a window or close to a door. The inside of the mould should be coated with whitewash.

The alternative method is to make a wooden pattern, which can either be shaped from a softwood log or made up from plywood. In the latter case the inside of the pattern must be adequately braced. As the pattern has to be lifted out of the sand, it should have some taper to it. The sand is placed in a rectangular wooden box, whose bottom follows the profile of the keel. The bottom planks should be covered with a sheet of asbestos and then a thin sheet of iron.

The pattern is placed on top of this, and casting sand is tamped down round it. The top of the pattern should be horizontal and exactly level with the top of the moulding box and the sand. The pattern should have handles for lifting.

Use either sheet lead or ingots, never old lead pipes, which might contain moisture and could explode when dropped into the melting pot. The molten metal can either be ladled into the mould or run in from an iron trough. The pouring must be continuous, so that the surface of the casting does not have time to solidify. Any scum forming on the surface of the molten metal should be skimmed off.

When the lead keel is cast, any irregularities in the casting can be shaved off with a chisel while the lead is still hot. It cuts easily. When the casting is cold, it can be put in position under the boat, and drilled for keel bolts through the existing holes in false keel and kelson.

Casting a keel is quite a difficult operation, and as any considerable weight of lead may be prohibitively expensive, the job is best left to the foundry, with the casting done in iron. However, trimming ballast could well be cast by the amateur following the procedure outlined above.

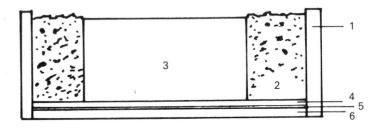

Casting a lead keel in a sand mould
in a wooden box:
1 Sides of the box
2 Sand
3 Lead
4 Iron sheet
5 Asbestos sheet
6 Bottom of box

Bona, Thames bawley, built at
Brightlingsea in 1903 and restored by
Stephen Swann and others in the 1970s

Glossary

Adze A tool like an axe with the blade set at right angles to the handle and curving towards it.

Apron A backing or strengthening timber inside the stempost.

Aqualevel A device for determining the water level of a vessel when chocked up out of the water.

Auger Long-shanked boring tool with cutting edge and screw point.

Bevel gauge See *Gauge*.

Bilges The curve of the hull where topsides and bottom planks meet; also the space inside the vessel below the floorboards.

Bitts Timbers set on or through the foredeck for belaying the anchor cable or mooring rope.

Bobstay Chain or wire from the end of the bowsprit to the stempost.

Bollard A firmly anchored post to which mooring ropes may be made fast.

Bolster A pad of wood to take chafe.

Boot topping A strip of different coloured paint along the waterline.

Boring bar A long steel bar with a thread at one end and an adjustable cutter in the middle.

Broadaxe A shipwright's axe for shaping heavy timbers.

Brow The chamfered top edge of clinker planks.

Bulwarks The sides of the ship above the deck.

Butt pad or strap A rectangular piece of planking used to back up a butt joint in topside or deck planking; also used for graving pieces that may have been let into the deck planking.

Cabin trunk A low deckhouse.

Carlines or carlings Structural timbers to which the sides of deck-houses are fastened, and into which the ends of the half-deck beams are fitted.

Capstan A revolving drum used for hauling in anchor cables, etc.

Carvel planking A method of planking a hull whereby the fore and aft planks fit edge to edge and are fastened to stout frames.

Cascophen A resorcin resin glue.

Caulking The method of filling the seams in deck or topsides with oakum or cotton.

Centreboard A board or plate that can be lowered through a slot in the keel of a sailing boat to reduce leeway.

Centreboard case A strongly supported wooden structure for housing the centreboard.

Chain plates Metal straps fastened to the topsides of a vessel and to which the shrouds are attached.

Channels Projecting timbers on the topsides of a boat for increasing the spread of the shrouds.

Cheekpieces Thickening pieces you fit, for instance, on either side of a lifeboat's sternpost, when drilling for a propeller shaft.

Chine The line where the topside joins the bottom planks of a flat- or V-bottomed boat.

Clamp or cramp   Wrought iron appliances for holding two or more pieces of timber while they are being glued or fastened.

Cleat   A two-armed wooden or metal deck fitting to which a rope may be belayed.

Clench   To fasten overlapping planking with copper nails turned over and hammered flat.

Clenched planking   A method of fastening overlapping planks by driving a copper nail through a bored hole, turned over and hammered flat across the grain of the timber.

Clinker planking   A method of fastening *overlapping* planks by driving a copper nail through a bored hole, fitting a roove over the end, cutting the nail short and burring it over the roove with a ball-pein hammer.

Coachroof   The roof over a deckhouse.

Coach screws   Heavy coarse-threaded screws with rectangular heads sometimes used for holding down an engine to its bearers.

Coamings   Raised planks enclosing cockpit or hatch.

Cope   The top piece of a moulding flask used in casting metal.

Counter   A rounded or square-ended stern that projects aft of the rudder.

Covering board   The outside deck plank that covers the timberheads.

Cranse iron   A circular iron band through which the bowsprit passes and to which the stays are attached.

Cringle   An eye in the bolt rope of a sail.

Crooks, grown   Bends formed by cutting a branching piece from the trunk of a tree.

Deadwood   A timber bolted on top of the keel, fore or aft, to take the ends of the frames and the lower planks.

Deck beams   Transverse beams from side to side of a vessel supporting the deck.

Deck shelf   The longitudinal timbers supporting the deck beams (American: *sheerclamp*).

Dolly   A solid metal object that is held against the outside of a boat when you are rooving or clenching fastenings.

Dory   A double-ended flat-bottomed rowing boat used on the Grand Banks for line fishing.

Drag   The bottom half of a moulding flask used in casting metal.

Drawknife   A tool like a large spokeshave, used for stripping spars.

Fairlead   A wooden or metal deck-fitting through which a rope may run.

False keel   The bottom timber of a keel, which can easily be replaced.

Fastenings   The iron, copper, bronze or wooden nails, screws or bolts used in fastening the planks and timbers of a vessel together.

Fay   To fit two timbers closely and exactly.

Feeler gauge   A gauge for measuring gaps in couplings.

Fender   A cushion of air-filled plastic or rope to protect the topsides of vessels lying alongside a quay or another vessel.

Fife rail   A rail carrying belaying pins, fitted near the mast just above the deck and to which the running rigging can be secured.

Flat points   Wrought-iron or mild-steel nails used for fastening planks to frames.

Flatty   A small flat-bottomed open boat.

Floors   The frames that support and tie the keel. *Short floors* are the timbers used to join the bottom of frames in fishing boats.

Frame clips   Metal plates used for joining frames and floors in dory construction.

Frames   The timbers or ribs to which the planks are fastened.

Freeboard   The amount of the side of the boat above the waterline.

Galvanic action   Electricity developed by chemical action.

Gammon iron   An iron loop fitting on the stemhead of a boat to hold the bowsprit.

Garboard   The plank next to the keel.

Gauge, bevel   Adjustable gauge for measuring angles.

Gauge, spar   A piece of wood with heart-shaped guides and two projecting scribing points fitted on the undersides. The points are fitted from each guide 0.293 times the distance between the guides.

Glues, resin   These are glues that have to be used with a hardening agent. In boatbuilding they have replaced natural glues. Beetle A, Aerolite 300 and Cascophen RS 216M are different brands and types of resin glues.

Graving piece   A piece of wood cut to shape and fitted flush into the deck to repair a hole or a worn section.

Gribble   Wood-boring crustacea, similar in appearance to woodlice.

GRP   Glass-reinforced plastic (so-called fibreglass).

Gudgeon   A metal eye on the after end of the sternpost to take the rudder pintle.

Gun punt   Long, slim, usually half-decked boats pointed at both ends and with very little freeboard. A gun can be mounted on the foredeck and used to slaughter duck. American gun punts are usually scow-shaped.

Gunwale   The timber that extends round the top edge of the topsides of a small craft.

Hammer, ball-pein   A hammer with a rounded head used for burring nails over rooves, etc.

Hatch   A covered opening in the deck.

Hawse pipe   The metal pipe through which the anchor cable runs.

Hog piece   A fore and aft timber on top of the keel of a vessel to which the garboards and frames are fastened.

Hoodends   The end of a plank where it fits into the rabbet cut in a stem, transom or sternpost.

Horse   A metal bar across the deck on which either the staysail or mainsheet blocks travel.

Horse, building   A trestle used for supporting such vessels as gun punts when they are being constructed.

Hounds   Wooden shoulders or mast bands at a point on the mast just about the full hoist of a gaff mainsail, to which the shrouds are attached.

Ingates   Channels in moulding.

Jig   A contrivance that holds any piece of wood and guides the tool operating it (eg for bevel and saw cuts).

Keel   The lowest longitudinal timber of a ship, to which the frames are fastened.

Kelson   The longitudinal timber (as in ships' lifeboats) which lies on top of the floors and to which the keel is bolted.

Kingplank   The centre plank of a foredeck.

Knees   *Hanging knees* are vertical supports for deck beams, etc; and *lodging knees* horizontal supports for deck beams, thwarts, etc.

Knightheads   The foremost pair of frames of a vessel.

Laminating   The joining of several pieces of thin wood in sandwich form with resin glues.

Lands   The bottom edges of the planks in clinker planking.

Lapstrake planking   See *Clinker planking*.

Leeboard Wooden or metal plate, attached to the sides of a flat-bottomed sailing boat, which can be lowered to reduce leeway.
Lining or ceiling Planking fastened inside the vessel over the timbers. Fishing boats usually have linings in their holds.
Lofting Drawing out the lines of a vessel before making templates.
LWL Length on waterline.
Moulding flask Two boxes, the cope and the drag, which can be filled with sand for casting metal objects.
Mute A tool for making tree-nails.
Nail sick When the fastenings in a hull have corroded and are loose, the hull is said to be nail sick.
Parral balls Wooden balls like large beads threaded on to lacings attached to the luff of the main or mizzen sail, to ease the passage of a sail up and down the mast.
Partners The deck beams on either side of the mast.
Pattern Thin pieces of wood (usually cedar) from which heavy timbers are shaped.
Pin rail A rail in which belaying pins are fixed.
Pintle The metal pin on a rudder, which slips into the gudgeon on the sternpost to form a hinge.
Pitch A natural mineral substance of dark colour, very viscid when subjected to heat, eg asphalt or bitumen. Can also be obtained from a distillation of coal tar.
Plumb bob A heavy weight at the end of a line used for accurate vertical lining up.
Rabbet or rebate A step-shaped reduction cut along the edge of a plank or timber to receive the edge or tongue of another plank.
Resin glues Glues that harden from the catalytic action of a special peroxide on polyester resin, which is a syrupy liquid. See also *Glues, resin*.
Risings The inboard strakes (for instance, in a lifeboat) used as supports for the thwarts.
Rivet A copper nail for holding planking to timbers, its headless end being beaten out over a roove.
Rooves or rubs Small round copper washers used in fastening.
Rubbing strake Protective planking to withstand chafe round the topsides of a vessel.
Rudder Flat wooden shape hinged to the sternpost and used for steering.
Rudder shaft The extension of the rudder blade, which passes through the counter, to which the tiller is attached.
Samson post A single bitt to which the anchor cable can be belayed.
Scarph To join timbers, beams or planks by halving their ends or cutting them away so that they fit into each other with overlapping.
Scarph, hooked A stepped scarph for locking two planks or timbers together.
Scribing The art of transferring the line of a plank or rabbet to another plank by the use of compass or dividers.
Service bolts Temporary fastenings.
Shaft log A stout hardwood chock fitted to the inside of the planking to take the stern-tube and inner gland bearing.
Sheave The wheel in the centre of a block or spar over which a rope may run.
Sheerlegs A primitive derrick made up from two spars crossed at the head, with a tackle suspended from this point for lifting heavy weights, stepping masts, etc.

Sheerstrake   The uppermost plank of a vessel's topsides.

Shelf   Longitudinal timber to which the ends of the beams are fastened.

Shims   Thin pieces of metal inserted as spacers and used between the fastening lugs of an engine and its bearers to get correct alignment.

Shiplap   A method of planking, with rebated edges to the planks, that unlike clinker (or lapstrake) planking presents smooth surfaces on both sides of the planks.

Shroud plate   A metal strap, fastened to the topsides of a vessel, to which the shrouds are attached.

Sister frames   New frames bolted to old faulty ones in a vessel to strengthen it.

Spanish windlass   A windlass made by inserting a rod or bolt through a bight of rope and then twisting it to serve as a lever.

Spiling   See *Scribing*.

Spline   A long thin piece of wood that can be bent to mark a fair curve.

Spreaders   Cross members on the mast to increase the spread of the rigging.

Sprue pins   Used to make airholes in the sand in a moulding flask.

Staghorn   A kind of bollard fitted over the bulwarks of a vessel.

Stanchion, bulwark   Support for the bulwarks.

Steambox   A contrivance used for steaming planks and timbers so that they can be bent into shape.

Stem   The foremost timber of the hull of a vessel, into which the planks are fitted.

Stemhead   The top of the stempost.

Sterns

  CANOE. A pointed counter stern.

  COLIN ARCHER. A Scandinavian type of pointed stern, more rounded than a lifeboat stern.

  COUNTER. A rounded stern that projects aft of the rudder post.

  LIFEBOAT. A pointed stern.

  SCANDINAVIAN. A pointed stern (like a lifeboat's) but with a full rounded deckline and flaring sections aft.

  TRANSOM. Made up of one or more planks athwart the sternpost, to which the ends of the planks are attached.

Stern-tube   The tube through the stern of a vessel housing the propeller shaft.

Stockholm tar   A wood tar (as opposed to a coal tar) used for the treatment of ropes and also as a preservative for timber.

Stopwater   A plug made of softwood, driven into a hole bored across a join to make it watertight.

Strake   One of the planks of a vessel's side or bottom.

Stringer   A fore and aft beam or girder.

Strop   A loop of rope or wire fitted round a block or spar.

Tabernacle   The support on deck in which the heel of the mast pivots.

Tar varnish   This can range from gasworks tar to slightly refined bitumastic paint. Useful for steel craft because of its anti-corrosive properties. As a substitute for anti-fouling, a mixture of 80 per cent tar varnish and 20 per cent creosote is tolerably effective.

Templates   These are cut out of hardboard or thin wood to show the profile of a timber.

Tencofix Dik   A proprietory underseal used in the Netherlands for motor cars, and suitable for caulking.

Tender   A yacht's dinghy, or any small vessel that serves a larger one.

Tenon   A joint for fastening two pieces of wood together.

Teredo   A wood-boring sea worm.

Thrust block   The bearings that take the thrust of the propeller.

Tie rods   Rods of bronze or steel used, for instance, to lock together the timbers of side decks.

Timberheads   The tops of the frames or timber

Timbers   The frames of a vessel.

Topsides   The planking of a vessel above the waterline.

Transom   A type of stern made up from one or more planks athwart the sternpost, to which the ends of the planks are attached.

Traveller   A ring that can be hauled along a spar or used on a horse to carry a sheet block.

Trowel cement   A filler made up in proprietory forms, used to smooth out abrasions or unevennesses in a surface that is to be painted.

Tumble-home   The inward inclination of a ship's topsides.

Waterline   The line at which a fully loaded vessel floats.

Waterway   A channel for the escape of water.

Web   A triangular piece of metal or wood for joining two girders or frames and beams in a ship.

Wheelhouse   A small cabin aft, housing the steering gear of a vessel.

Windlass   A revolving barrel fitted athwartships in the bows of a smack and used for hauling in the anchor.

Acknowledgements

I would like to thank many friends for their help and advice over the problems of repairing old wooden boats. Much of this information was gathered together when I was working on my two previous books, *Vintage Boats* and *Small Craft Conversion*. The rest of it has come through many years of messing about *with* boats.

I would like to thank particularly the Woodbridge shipwrights Keith Cutmore, Philip Gooch and Frank Knights, and the late Robert Brewster, who worked with them. I would also like to thank Michael Frost, who gave me unstinted help over his description of his rebuild of the Maldon oyster dredger *Boadicea*; Roy Wallace for telling me about methods used in rebuilding the Friendship sloop *Estella A*; Ernst Weigleb for his description of reframing his Friendship sloop *Chrissy*; Maurice Griffiths, GM, for the loan of his drawings of hatches and much advice; Francis Jones for the drawings of the construction of hollow spars and tabernacles; John Perryman, ARINA, for information about fungicides; Peter Brown for his notes about surveying; Roger Finch for his detailed drawings and descriptions of casting processes; and Keith Mirams for his admirable photographs.

Finally my lasting gratitude is due to the late William Porter of Manningtree, who was my first instructor in boat repair and who taught me much about the pleasures of such work.